SEARCHING FOR ORPHEUS

personal essays about music and the brain

by Lee R. Harris

Dedicated to all of those who have brought music into my life and to my wife Terri, who is my song.

ISBN 978-9861320-5-6

Keywords: 1. Music 2. Brain 3. Psychology

Chapter   Page

PREFACE

These essays are born of curious mediocrity. Music has always been an interest of mine, but fifty years of effort has yielded only modest ability to play an instrument. I was fortunate that other interests led me to become a veterinarian, where I was more suited for success. But music continues to exert a pull on me, leading me to think about melody, harmony, and rhythm in many different ways.

The brain has always held a special interest for me as well, and my dog and cat patients with neurologic problems have given me fascinating things to ponder. Considering the different modes of perception and processing in animals has broadened my concepts of mind and communication.

Music reveals details of the human brain's functioning that language is unable to express. No other neurologic process is distributed as widely across the brain as music, and musical perception persists, even after memory fades, muscular control falters, and our senses fail.

I am interested in what psychologists have learned about music and I have read widely on the subject, but personal experience sometimes reveals perspectives that go beyond what science tells us. My own involvement in playing and listening to music is vital to understanding these subjects, so I have drawn liberally from my own story in my search for musical insights.

My motivation for exploring the neurologic basis for music is partly selfish. I find music interesting but my ability to play the guitar, piano, bass, cello, violin, flute, and other instruments that litter my office is limited. I am always looking for a musical "hack", some shortcut that might overcome my lack of talent. I wish I could find the magic powers of Orpheus, the musician of myth that used his harp to unlock the doors of Hades in his search for his great love.

Even the ability to appreciate music emotionally eludes me. Harmonic structure, melodic nuance, and rhythmic complexity fascinate me, but music has never brought me to tears or joyful ecstasy; I continue to search for these musical experiences but realize that understanding the sounds may have to be enough.

I am not a brilliant neurologist like Oliver Sacks, nor a gifted musician like Leonard Bernstein (or Leonard Cohen, or even Leonard Nimoy); I am simply an interested amateur. My chosen profession taught me how to trace the routes of nerves with a neurologic exam and how to read the basics of a brain MRI, but it is my interest in music that leads me to wonder how the electro-chemical signals exchanged by nerve cells create the invisible force of music. Let me share a few things I have learned.

1

TAKE ME TO THE RIVER

After successful surgery for a benign pancreatic tumor, Andrew Schuman unexpectedly went into anaphylactic shock and cardiac arrest, his brain receiving only a trickle of oxygen for the next 17 minutes. He spent the following eight days in a coma.

Once Andrew regained consciousness, his grasp on life was precarious; the numbers on the intensive care monitors lurched to the very edge of survivability. On a hunch, Andrew's wife Wendy brought a CD player to the Surgical Intensive Care Unit and put Bach's St Mathew's Passion, one of Andrew's favorite pieces, into the player. With the right earpiece in his ear and the left earpiece in her own, she pressed play.

After thirty minutes, Andrew's blood pressure and vitals started to stabilize and remained strong. He was in critical condition for three more days, but he had returned to the land of the living.

Andrew and Wendy, as well as the extensive medical records, credit Bach's music with rescuing Andrew from a sudden descent into the underworld. It is appropriate that music saved Andrew, as he was a professional classical guitarist and music was his life.

As he began his recovery, Andrew found that his brain was largely intact, despite the prolonged cerebral ischemia that was expected to cause problems with speech, movement, and understanding. It wasn't until he returned home and picked up his guitar that he was hit with a devastating discovery: He couldn't remember any of the music that he had played over decades of doing concerts and restaurant gigs in New York City. He had always played from memory, with hundreds of pieces in his repertoire; now they were all gone, except for six pieces (two classical, two Spanish, and two Beatles tunes), which he had learned before he was 20 years old. His amnesia for musical pieces persisted; he was never able to memorize new music, no matter how hard he tried, and the music that he had previously stored in memory was gone, never to return.

Strangely, Andrew's abilities to read music and play the guitar returned quickly. His neurologist explained that oxygen deprivation tends to damage the areas of the brain that are most used, and Andrew had spent his life playing music from memory.

In neuro-anatomic terms, memory is most at home in the hippocampi, the seahorse-shaped centers deep in each side of the brain. Both of Andrew's hippocampi were devastated, and it was as if his music library had burned down. But the ability to play music draws on widely distributed parts of the brain, and music recognition and performing ability are often preserved when the brain is decimated by trauma, stroke, or dementia.

Andrew had experienced the power of music in his own life, and his book, "Waking the Spirit", tells how his personal journey inspired him to offer his services as an informal music therapist, playing his classical guitar at the bedside of hospitalized patients with a variety of life-threatening conditions. He is the resident musician at the Surgical Intensive Care Unit of Mount Sinai Beth Israel Hospital in New York City, bringing his gift of healing to those who need it most. Relinquishing his own gift of memorizing music has forced him to play from the written page; in a way, he outsourced music memory from his hippocampi to notes printed on paper, but he retained the deeply ingrained patterns in his motor cortex, his visual and auditory centers, and his hands. Even when we can't remember, our experiences and skills still live within us.

Forgetfulness is as old as antiquity. The Greeks, of course, had a myth to explain the erasing of memories. The River Lethe was one of the five mythical rivers that flowed through the Hades underworld and it carried the power to obliterate the stored memories of life, tragedy, triumph, and knowledge. After death, according to Greek lore, a person was required to drink from the River Lethe on their journey to the underworld, eliminating all earthly memories before reincarnation. Members of a cult dedicated to Orpheus were urged to do whatever they could to avoid the waters of the Lethe after they died, so that they could carry their memories forward into the next life. The metaphor of a river seems appropriate for memory loss—the onward flow of life, whether as a rushing torrent or a meandering slough, takes its toll on our remembering minds, carrying our memories away piece by piece.

There is a balance between the acquisition of knowledge and its fading, and Greek myths also told of Lethe's sister river, Mnemosyne, which had the opposite effect: those who drank its waters would remember everything. Modern psychology has its own name for people that drink from the Mnemosyne: A highly superior autobiographical memory is termed Hyperthymesia, and those rare people who possess it (actress Marilu Henner is the most famous example) find it exhausting. Those of us who worry about our unreliable memories might envy the ability of those with perfect memory to recall everything, but being unable to forget carries its own thorns. It is said that time heals all wounds, but it is actually forgetfulness, not time, that heals. Human experience is filled with pain, disappointment, and regret, whether it is a painful auto accident, a traumatic romantic breakup, or the regret of a missed opportunity that haunts us. The cure for regret is to forget, a luxury denied those whose minds cannot be purged of the daily details of their lives. A few drops from the Lethe would be a blessing when remembering is worse than forgetting.

A sip from the Mnemosyne, however, might be welcome when we struggle to remember what we went to the grocery store to buy. I have reached the age where every unsuccessful attempt to recall a name or event induces apprehension that I am "losing it". Watching my mother as her Alzheimer's Disease progressed raised the question of who a person is when the events and people of their life are no longer present in their mind.

Despite the promise of "living in the moment" that is sought for in meditation (and perhaps in music), we are apprehensive when the present moment becomes just a small island in the middle of a river of forgetting. Every older adult wonders about their memory, and forgetfulness seems to be a topic that always arises when any group of 50+ seniors gather. Although we are promised that our brain has unlimited storage potential, we sometimes feel like the student in a Far Side cartoon who raises his hand in class and asks "May I be excused? My brain is full."

After a prolonged open heart surgery seven years ago, I seemed to notice obvious (to me) memory problems. My doctor insists that "pumphead" (the term nurses use for cognitive damage from the heart-lung machine) isn't a real thing, and he suggests that perhaps I should get used to writing everything down.

There really isn't any effective treatment for memory loss, anyway.

There are musical implications, however. Is it worth spending hours practicing music if the learning doesn't persist? Isn't improvement the purpose of practicing?

As I became more aware of my memory problems, I was determined to swim against the current of forgetfulness by memorizing a single piece of music. Every guitarist has their one "guitar store piece", something impressive that they can play from memory if someone at a party hands them a guitar and says "play us something" (this never actually happens, but you want to be ready, just in case) or if the guitarist stops into a music store to buy a couple of guitar picks and decides to try out one of the vintage guitars on the wall (this does actually happen, and you want to be ready).

I had learned to play JS Bach's Bourree from the Lautensuite in E minor when I was first learning to play classical guitar, but I had never memorized it. This seemed like a good test case, since it consists of a plain treble melody and a bass countermelody, and the music is familiar (this piece even enjoyed some popularity in the 60's, when the rock band Jethro Tull recorded a version). I applied all sorts of mnemonic techniques: I tried to visualize the written music, I analyzed the harmonic progression as a roadmap, I tried playing two measures over and over without looking at the music, I tried learning the treble and bass line separately, singing one part as I played the other, hoping that my ear would remind me of the next note. After months of work, I never retained more than eight bars of the Bourree. Most discouragingly, the ability to commit fragments of the music to memory did not improve over the course of time. It was as if my guitar had been dipped into the River Lethe. And yet I hoped that struggling against the impossibility of memorizing the Bourree might be doing something good for my brain.

When memory and dementia experts study various activities and their effects on preserving cognitive abilities, they find that the "use it or lose it" effect of a mental challenge varies with the type of activity. Reading or doing crossword puzzles has only mild protective effects on the brain, while activities that require "thinking forward" to what is about to happen have a marked effect. In one study, rats were trained to blink when a tiny puff of air was directed at their face, accompanied by a beep. Then they separated the tone and the pulse of air by a second or two, and the rats learned to blink a second or two after they heard the tone, thinking forward to predict the on-coming event. This process seemed to strengthen the rats memories and thinking abilities more than just blinking into the wind.

As memory enhancing activities go, it seems like music, particularly playing music, and more particularly improvising in a group context, should be more powerful than doing Sudoku or reading.

Listening to music, or moving to music, has been used therapeutically for the memory-impaired, perhaps because the music creates expectations in time that either resolve or remain suspended. Brain scientists also point out that musical perception and ability are more widely distributed in the brain than language or most other activities. A stroke in Broca's Language Area of the left cerebral cortex leaves the unfortunate patient completely without words, but there is no similar area where a lesion will rob a person of musical awareness. In fact, as we will explore in a later essay, damaging or temporarily inactivating the left side of the brain may actually release musical passions and abilities.

Music therapy for dementia takes advantage of the wide distribution of tunes in the brain to make connections to memories that are still present, but inaccessible. In Ellen Sanger's book on reversing the aging process, "Counterclockwise", she tells of taking elderly patients who were mentally and physically disabled on a two week retreat during which they were surrounded by music from their younger years (as well as other triggers to make them feel the way they did in their youth). The threads of the old melodies tugged at the memories and emotions of the patients' younger selves, and both mental and physical tests revealed a rolling back of the years.

Still, my doubts persist. As a mediocre amateur musician, is my practice time spent in vain as age makes its withdrawals from my memory faster than learning deposits new skills? After all, Plato reminded us that "all learning is remembering".

An encouraging perspective comes from another account of severe amnesia. In "The Perpetual Now", author Su Meck follows Lonnie Sue Johnson, an artist who suffered a viral infection of her temporal lobes which left her with profound retrograde and anterograde amnesia. She couldn't remember any event from her past, nor form any new memories. Every moment was new and temporary. Researchers visited Lonnie Sue regularly, with the morbid curiosity that only neurologists can muster for the wrecked brain. When they learned that Lonnie Sue had been a talented amateur violist, they saw an opportunity to probe the relationship of music and memory. Like Andrew Schulman, Lonnie Sue was still able to read music and find the fingerings and bowings on her instrument, and yet she had no memory of the music she played.

A composer was asked to write a piece for the viola, using common classical vocabulary but distinct from any composition that she might have heard or played. On one of their weekly visits they asked her to learn the music, which she did, asked her if she had ever heard it before, which she hadn't, and recorded her playing it for twenty minutes. Every week when they returned for a visit, the entire scene was replayed: Lonnie Sue was asked to play the piece, she said that she had no recollection of it, and then she played it for twenty minutes while being recorded.

When the recordings were evaluated blindly by several musicologists, they noted that Lonnie Sue's mastery of the piece improved over time. Practice, even if you don't remember doing it, shows results; the journey might indeed be the destination.

When Pablo Casals, one of the great cellists of the 20th century, turned ninety years old, he claimed that he practiced for two hours every morning. Asked why, the maestro replied "I think I am starting to make a little progress". Maybe that is all that any of us can hope for.

2

MUSIC OF THE HEMISPHERES

Joann Brackeen doesn't look like a jazz pianist. Her spray of frizzy hair and oversized glasses give her the appearance of a slightly crazy ninth-grade English teacher. But Ms. Brackeen has serious credentials as both a teacher and a performer. One night she slipped into a club where the Miles Davis Quintet was playing and noticed that the piano seat was vacant. In the middle of Miles' solo she walked over to the piano and sat down, comping for the trumpeter and then launching into her own improvisation as he finished up. Miles barely looked up as Joann continued to sit in until the end of the set; then he walked over and growled "My pianist walked out and I go out on tour tomorrow. Be at the train station at noon tomorrow."

I met Ms. Brackeen when she was giving a music workshop for students and amateurs at Seattle's Experience Music Project. I had been playing bass for a year or so, and I struggled (as I still do) to know what notes to play when accompanying other musicians. I knew my scales and chords, but meshing the right bass line with the improvisation of other musicians was difficult, and years of music theory study didn't help me find the right sounds.

As Ms. Brackeen was demonstrating how she might re-harmonize a jazz standard by substituting different chords for the usual harmonies, I asked her: "When you are playing with a trio, what notes do you want to hear from the bassist? Do you like to hear the roots and fifths of the chords, or are any of the scale notes appropriate? What if the bass wants to add something melodic that isn't in the regular chords?" What I really wanted to know is: "What are you thinking about while you play and improvise?"

With a bemused smile she answered, "When I am performing, I have no idea what the chords are. I just play."

This puzzled me. Joann certainly knew all of the theory behind the music—she had taught at Rutgers University, Berklee School of Music, and The New School. She could not be unaware of the harmonic rules that made her music sound the way that it did. What did it feel like to play so masterfully while being unaware of how she was doing it?

This puzzle remains mostly unsolved, but in my search I have asked many other musicians what they are thinking, what they are hearing and experiencing as they perform. They usually find it difficult to express their actions in words, but it seems that there must be more than just understanding music theory to turn notes into music; something mysterious is going on in the brain.

I found hints to the answer in Iain McGilchrist's massive book, "The Master and His Emissary: The Divided Brain and the Making of the Western World". Dr. McGilchrist is a psychiatrist and neuroimaging researcher who has been exploring the differences and interactions of the two separate sides of our brain. Pop psychology embraced the dichotomy of right brain vs left brain when early studies showed that the two sides of our cerebral cortex have different strengths and weaknesses. Soon people were being labelled right-brain dominant (creative, wholistic) or left-brain dominant (linear, analytical) and the differences were being used to explain everything from learning disabilities to political persuasions. McGilchrist warns that this is a gross oversimplification.

It isn't that those ideas were wrong, McGilchrist notes in the introduction of his book, but that the truth is more complex, and even more powerful. The right and left hemispheres of the cerebral cortex do operate with different (and often opposing) methods, but they also co-operate, with communication constantly crossing the corpus callosum, the neural bridge between the sides, to create, add, edit, and put into words the thoughts that emerge from the opposite side. The left brain certainly carries out some "right-brain-ish" functions, and vice versa, but the central idea is that there are competing priorities and strategies within the brain that can be described by the shorthand of "right" and "left". This updated view of the "two brains" has benefitted from the non-invasive imaging that has become the favored tool of brain researchers (functional MRI and PET scanning). Further insights have been gained from patients with intractable epilepsy who have had their corpus callosum severed to prevent seizures from spreading from one side of the brain to the other, creating a truly divided brain.

The second half of McGichrist's magnum opus deals with how the balance between the two cerebral hemispheres has influenced Western civilization over the past three thousand years, but for the purposes of my inquiry the heart of McGilchrist's thesis can be summarized simply: The right hemisphere gathers general "big picture" information, full of context and connections. This information is sent across the corpus callosum to the left brain for detailed, stepwise investigation. The left side plays a consultant role, providing sequential analysis and adding language, a skill mostly lacking in the right brain. All of this updated information is then sent back to the right brain to increase the accuracy of the larger picture before action is taken. The right brain notes the contrast between the world as described by the left brain and the world as it actually is, creating humor and metaphor.

This seems like a good system, each half playing to its strength to provide a balanced approach that is greater than either part. The problem as McGilchrist sees it is that the left brain (the "emissary" in his title) specializes in certainty and language, and tells the right brain "I've got this, and I can take it from here." Since the left possesses the ability to put things into words and is completely confident in its own theories, it may dominate the interchange without realizing that it doesn't see the whole picture.

How does this rivalry between the hemispheres apply to music? Language finds its home mostly in the left hemisphere; a small stroke in Broca's area of the left cortex can result in loss of the power of speech (aphasia). Music is more widely distributed, but predominantly in the right half of the brain. People with widespread damage to the brain, as in dementia, often retain music perception and appreciation, even after memory and cognitive functions have faded. Music therapists often use songs to connect with the mentally disabled, grasping whatever threads of humanity that remain with remembered melodies. While the left brain deals with objects and things that can be manipulated, the right brain is for living things: people, dogs, and curiously, musical instruments. Whether this last is because of the fact that we cradle a guitar or a saxophone in our hands or because they produce music is not clear, but even a visual image of a violin activates blood flow to the music side of our brain more than to the side of language and things.

What interests me is how listening to music is influenced by the hemispheres. If the right side listens for context, emotion, and the relationship of one note to another, it is easy to guess that it receives music as a whole experience—it is what it is, entering our perception directly. We don't have to think about it.

The left, on the other hand, concentrates on the details; it pays more attention to individual melody notes and less to their relationships to the other voices in the music. It seeks the rules that create the patterns and knows what it likes; when taking music theory class in college, we were drilled with guidelines like "when the melody jumps up by a large interval it must not continue going up but should come back down in a stepwise fashion." I don't know if that is how Mozart thought, but as students we were reprimanded if we violated the rules. The left hemisphere has a lot to think about before it reports back to the right hemisphere, where the combined efforts are expressed as music. If both sides are in balance, the details and rules add luster to the music coming from the right side of the brain. But it doesn't always work that way.

I picture the right saying to the left "Don't you just love the sound that the orchestra is making?" But the left has to take things apart, replying "I notice that the brass instruments are louder than the violins, but they don't seem to play as much—is that because the players tire out from using their lip muscles? I hear the same little group of notes being repeated frequently, as if the composer thinks we didn't hear it the first time. How do the conductor's arm movements relate to the sounds that the musicians produce? And I read that the sonata is supposed to have three different sections; have they gotten to the recapitulation yet?" "Just sit back and listen," whispers the right; "let the sounds wash over you." But the left, sure of itself, stands up to leave: "I have heard enough to understand it all. Let's go". Hopefully the right brain has the car keys.

I have experienced just this sort of chatter. A few years ago I went to hear the Preservation Hall Jazz Band, the modern torchbearers for New Orleans jazz. Tuba player Allen Jaffe had formed the band at the historic French Quarter venue in 1961, using an all-star group of "N'awlins" musicians, ages 60 to 90 years. Obviously, none of the original members were still playing now, although the repertoire was very traditional. Most of the current bandmates were relatives: sons, nephews, and even grandsons of the original members.

The music was full of the joyous rhythms and traditions of the Crescent City. But as I listened, I recognized that the chords the pianist played were more complex than would have been used in the heyday of Louis Armstrong or King Oliver. There it was, a 13th chord when a simple 7th chord would have been sufficed. And that lick the trumpeter threw in was more bebop than Second Line. These observations were interesting, but they didn't serve my musical enjoyment very well. I had to wrestle the experience away from my left brain and return it to my right in order to let the music flow, tap my feet, and feel the groove. And just in time, as I laughed along with the trumpet player when he repeated one of the saxophonist's phrases back to him with a sour note at the end.

If experiencing music in a wholistic way is the soul of music, what does that mean to the musician who practices countless hours to master the music? Brain studies confirm that professional musicians use the left side more than the casual listener or novice music student does. Analysis allows the skilled musician to use the left brain to craft a more complex, detailed performance. This is as it should be; if Claude Debussy had not sat at his piano trying different scales, he would not have arrived at the idea of constructing his compositions from a scale of whole tones, rather than the whole tone/half tone patterns of major and minor scales. But his right brain had to take these new harmonic theories in turn and add the context of melancholy and world-weariness to create his haunting Claire de Lune.

Perhaps the musical primacy of the right hemisphere accounts for why folk musics, untainted by the analytical detail of the left, are universally enjoyed, even across cultural lines. Classical composers have used the direct emotional appeal of folk melody in their symphonies; Dvorak's New World Symphony would not have achieved its popularity if the melody from the folk spiritual "Goin' Home" was missing. Popular music (especially in the earlier forms of Grand Ol' Opry country, New Orleans jazz, blues-based rock, and indie singer-songwriter music) has also benefitted from the directness and simplicity of musicians that have never attended music school or taken a music theory class. Three chords and lots of emotion are still a successful formula.

But progressive musicians continue to use their left sides to search for new sounds and ways of communicating, asking the left brain to understand how a new harmony is built, or how the rules of counterpoint allow two voices to complement one another. Although music is most at home in the right hemisphere, a trip to the left hemisphere is like a vacation in Europe, bringing new perspectives and observations. Coming home to the right hemisphere completes the trip with a sense of belonging and completeness.

Maybe this is what pianist Joann Brackeen was trying to say in answer to my question: No matter how thoroughly she understood the chords and scales in her music, the actual act of performing depended on her right brain, intuitive and driven by what she heard in her own mind and the context of the sounds around her. Creativity starts in one country, travels across a landscape of theory, and is then released into the world of experience as an intuitive stream of music after completing its return trip to the right hemisphere.

In his book, McGilchrist makes the argument that our culture has allowed the left hemisphere to dominate our lives and culture, to the detriment of our society and ourselves. Science has created unheard of advances with its detailed descriptions and its quest for certainty, but often fails to use its fruits to increase our humanity. Technology has solved everything, except for how people can cooperate and be kind to each other. The "rule of law" has become the "law of rules", with less attention paid to why a regulation has been made and more to arguing over how the regulation should be enforced. And language always claims to have the last word. But even a linguist and philosopher such as Ludwig Wittgenstein realized the limitations of words when he wrote that "language is inadequate to express reality".

We needn't despair, however, as McGilchrist finds hope: "One possibility is that music, which brought us together before language existed, might even now prove effective in regenerating commonality, avoiding the need for words that have become devalued, or for which we have become too cynical. Let us not forget that it was with music that Orpheus moved stones."

We have the means, just beneath a thin layer of bone on the right side of our skulls, to combine logic and language with context, intuition, and wholistic perspective. We can restore our ability to deal with the world of experience without categorizing and reducing everything to mind vs body, us vs them, humans vs all other life. Music's greatest power may be to speak from the right hemisphere of empathy, humor, harmony, and beauty.

Claude Debussy knew as much, even without brain imaging or neurologic research: "There is no theory. You need just to listen."

3

NOTHING MORE THAN FEELINGS

"Auditory cheesecake". That phrase has caused more acrimonious argument than any other single statement in Steven Pinker's career. Pinker is an influential psychologist with world-class credentials: Professor at Stanford. Harvard, and MIT, author of eight books for "general audiences" as well as dozens of scholarly articles. What set off Pinker's detractors was his assessment of the biologic value of music as a human activity.

In his book, "How the Mind Works" (which attempts to explain everything cerebral), Pinker states: "As far as biologic cause and effect are concerned, music is useless. Music appears to be a pure pleasure technology, a cocktail of recreational drugs that we ingest through the ear to stimulate a mass of pleasure circuits at once." Auditory cheesecake. And if we missed his point, he adds that "music communicates nothing but formless emotion."

Biologists always search for some evolutionary benefit to any behavior that an organism displays, and an ability like music that takes so much time and energy and is found across all human cultures must have some survival value in order to justify the brain functions that support it. This is the "adaptionist" position: Music evolved to attract the opposite sex, strengthen social bonds through ritual song and dance, and reinforce territorial claims (I envision a "Battle of the Bands" at UN headquarters, but they probably mean the intimidating threat of an entire tribe chanting as they attack their neighbors, or maybe the sound of bagpipes, which were originally used to scare away enemy armies).

Those benefits of music seem plausible, but scholarly anthropologists and psychologists don't accept music as an evolutionary benefit. Steven Pinker definitely sits on the "non-adaptionist" side of the debate.

Aniraddh Patel studies music and cognition at the Neurosciences Institute in La Jolla and he proposes a more nuanced view, calling music a "transformative technology of the mind". He suggests that music is a human invention, like fire or writing, rather than a biologic adaptation, but it provides both musical and non-musical benefits and is capable of causing physical changes in a number of brain areas over a person's lifetime. These changes are a consequence of how music engages the brain, but not a cause of musical behaviors.

All of these origin-of-music theories treat music as a poor stepchild of language, whether legitimate, illegitimate, or adopted. Language came first and music was a later development that hitched a ride on skills designed for the spoken word. Archeologist Steven Mithen sees it differently. In his book, "The Singing Neanderthal", he develops the idea that music existed for hundreds of thousands of years before language. Music before words.

Using various strands of modern knowledge about the brain, language, and music, as well as evidence from prehistory, Mithen weaves his theory that early hominids may have developed enhanced musical abilities long before Homo sapiens started talking.

Neanderthals are the best known of the human relatives that preceded our own species. These early people managed to survive and thrive for 350,000 years in Europe, lasting through the ice ages. They became extinct 40,000 years ago, but not before mating, mingling, and sharing with their cousins from Africa who were destined to become modern humans. Although language as we know it is presumed to have developed with Homo sapiens, it seems likely that the earlier hominids used their own communication system, and it sounded a lot like music.

The Neanderthals were far from the stupid slack-jawed cavemen of stereotype. Physical signs shows that they had large brains and tool-making talents. Indirect evidence suggests that they had areas of deep knowledge of their world and a degree of cultural sophistication. Neanderthals probably possessed expert "domain specific" knowledge about their environment but lacked the "cognitive fluidity" needed to connect these areas of expertise in the way that modern humans do. They knew how to find food, make tools, build shelters, and maintain the close social bonds needed to live in successful groups. Mithen claims that these "pre-lingual" hominids likely had a well-developed system of music-based expression.

Several developments allowed the development of musical communication. The first was anatomic: The upright posture of walking on two legs moved the position of the larynx so that a flexible range of tones could be produced which weren't possible for other primates. You need an instrument if you are going to make music.

Secondly, social groups grew larger among our human ancestors, increasing the need for a means of establishing alliances and resolving conflicts. In other primates grooming serves this function, but in larger groups a less "hands-on" approach was needed, and the newly evolved vocal tract was well-suited to the role.

Early musical communication, although it provided some foundation for later language, was not language in the modern sense. It was distinguished, according to Mithen, by being holistic (entire unique strings of sounds describing specific situations), rather than compositional (built from individual sounds that could be combined into a longer messages, words in search of grammar). Musical expression would have been non-referential (not naming objects, but expressing an emotional description of what an experience felt like). Mithen coins a term for this: Hmmmm, or

Holistic (expressing the feeling of a situation)
manipulative (intended to influence others)
multi-modal (inseparable from gestures and movement)
musical (changes in pitch and rhythm to express more information)
    and
mimetic (inviting imitation and response)

The high value of the Hmmmm system of communication would have encouraged it to become more complex and sophisticated with use, given the large brain that Neanderthals had developed. It is believed (based on the abilities of babies and non-verbal autistics) that Neanderthals had "absolute pitch", making them more sensitive to specific sound frequencies than most modern humans. The content would have consisted of emotional information, rather than nouns and verbs, but it would still have been sufficient to tell a story: Imagine the Neanderthal man whose child was killed in a wolf attack. While the episode was taking place, the father would have expressed a complex emotional utterance (with accompanying gestures). When the father returned, distraught, to his tribe's camp, he might repeat and embellish the similar utterances, telling the story with musical and emotional content without needing to use specific words for "wolf" or "son"; his listeners understood the dangers of their environment and would easily have grasped the gist of the story, as well as the father's state of mind and need for comforting.

More evidence for the development of music before words comes from modern human infants. Studies of "Infant-Directed Speech" note that babies respond to musical sounds long before they respond to spoken words. Mothers across the world intuitively use sing-song vocalizations to engage their babies. Some of these studies even include "Pet-Directed Speech", which is very similar to the way that we talk to infants (just try saying "who's a good doggy?" in flat tone of voice!). Without words, the melody is the message.

Life was harsh for stone-age tribes. Life expectancy was less than 35 years and parents and grandparents were often not alive to care for their slow-maturing children, making the social bonds between tribe members critical to survival. Group singing and dancing promoted social commitment in a very real way; instead of simply belonging to a group, the singer became the group, as a gathering of combined voices blurs the lines of individuality. The singers cease to hear themselves as separate from the sea of sound produced by other voices; the tribe that sang as one was more likely to care for each other's children. It takes a village—and a song.

But could music be a language of its own?

When it comes to the definition of language, people are very nearsighted. We have a tendency to presume that languages other than our own are somehow more primitive, expressing simpler thoughts. Until recently, the sign language used by deaf persons was imagined to be nothing but a crude collection of gestures without grammar. The richness of expression conveyed by the location, size, and emphasis of the signs was overlooked. Oliver Sacks, in his book "Hearing Voices", tells of visiting the island of Martha's Vineyard, where many of the early settlers had a genetic form of deafness and it was normal for all residents to use sign as well as their own languages. Hearing impairment has since become rare, but the tradition of using sign along with English has persisted. On his visit, Sacks joined a group older people who were conversing in English on the front porch of a country store when one of them stopped speaking and started using sign to tell what appeared to be a story, after which the others laughed appreciatively. It turns out that some things are just funnier in sign.

The proposed prehistoric language of Hmmmm seems even farther from our modern verbal language than sign language. It is hard for us to imagine it having the power of the spoken word, but this is more a limitation of our imagination than a limitation of the communication itself. We are used to language that is specific, individual, and referential, while the musical language of pre-linguistic humans was more wholistic and contained direct expressions of emotion.

Even though music and language are stored separately in the brain, they are connected, which helps the recall of each (quick, what letter comes after "r" in the alphabet? —did you have to sing part of the alphabet song?) There is a story about Coleman Hawkins, the great tenor saxophonist of the Swing Era.

Hawk was improvising one of his elaborate solos over the chord changes of a well-known standard when he stopped abruptly. When one of his band-mates asked him why he quit playing, he replied "I forgot the words to the song."

The power of music, now as in the Ice Ages, lies in emotion. Emotion was once considered an unworthy subject of study, and it is still treated like an inconvenient weird uncle of the rational mind. Don't get all emotional, we are told. Get a grip on yourself. Think about what you are doing. But rational thinking is not really how our minds operate.

In his book, "How We Decide", Jonah Lehrer describes the central role of emotion in our ability to make decisions. He describes patients who had damage to the emotional centers of their brains while fully retaining their ability to reason. Although they were able to weigh the pros and cons of their options in great detail, they were unable to take action because they couldn't make up their minds. In reality, decisions come from the emotions and the rational frontal cortex simply makes up reasons to explain and justify the decisions after the fact; we call it rationalization. Even our language suggests that we should rely more on our feelings: Trust your instincts, we are told, go with your gut, rely on your intuition.

If we were more fluent in the language of emotion, we might discover that our feelings are more rich, complex, and useful than we think. We tend to paint emotions as simple primary colors; we feel angry, or sad, or happy. We don't have an emotional designation for the feeling of watching the sun come up as we drink our coffee and consider the unpleasant issues that we will need to deal with as soon as we arrive at work. Emotions may not be considered the equivalent of thoughts, but they under-lie our understanding of the world and prompt us to action.

The primacy of emotion has been explored eloquently by neuroscientist Antonio Damasio in his book, "The Feeling Of What Happens". Not only is emotion central to decision making, but it forms the basis of consciousness itself. All of the interactions of daily life depend on it. Damasio describes emotions as "what homeostasis feels like". He views the emotions not only as a driver of motivation and action, but also as the mind's link to the body (his previous book, "Descarte's Error", deals with the obsolete idea of a separation of body and mind). The idea of music as the emotion-centered first language of mankind is in harmony with his view of emotion as the root of consciousness, and "consciousness was invented so that we could know life".

We may not be able to imagine what the music of our distant ancestors sounded like before it was diminished by the development of language, but we can listen for the echoes of our first language in Mozart's Requiem in D Minor, Miles Davis' So What, or Led Zeppelin's Stairway to Heaven.

The rich complexity of being human lies hidden in an ancient language; in the words of TS Elliot, it exists in:

> "Music heard so deeply
> That it is not heard at all, but you are the music
> While the music lasts."

All together now, everybody sing "Hmmmm". And pass the cheesecake.

4

MAKING THE LEAP

The rooftop of the next building is eight feet away, but there is no time to calculate the angle and distance as you sprint at full speed toward the edge. You jump, guessing at your trajectory, hoping to land smoothly on the other side. You only hope that you can make the leap.

This is roughly the apprehension faced by an amateur pianist attempting a blind two octave leap in a difficult Chopin composition.

In his book, "Play It Again", Alan Rushbridger details his mid-life quest to master Chopin's intimidating piano Ballade #1 while stealing practice time from his frenzied day job as editor-in-chief of the Guardian newspaper during troubled times. Setting a goal of playing the piece in public within a year, Rushbridger chips away at each challenging page of the music until he comes to the daunting coda, fast, syncopated, explosive, with trapeze-like two octave leaps in the right hand as the left hand retreats in the opposite direction. This action happens so rapidly that there is no time to glance down at his hands to see where they are going. The pianist might as well be leaping from rooftop to rooftop, relying on some sixth sense to guide his hoped-for landing.

This feeling is familiar to any musician whose ambitions are larger than their talent. After my children left for college I was determined to become a competent pianist; ultimately I was unsuccessful, in part because I could not keep my eyes on the written music. I could only find the right keys by sight; there was no feeling of where in space my hands were traveling. It became obvious that watching my hands was not the way that real piano players navigate the keyboard. Seeing is often a poor way to find what you are seeking, and I could almost wish that I was blind.

The list of famous pianists without vision is long and familiar: Ray Charles, Stevie Wonder, Art Tatum, George Shearing, Marcus Roberts. Perhaps being blind might even confer an advantage at the keyboard.

Searching through videos of blind pianists, I found their ability to find the notes without sight even more baffling. When Ray Charles sits down to play Georgia On My Mind, it appears that he doesn't even touch the piano to orient himself before reaching out to play the opening chords. Watching blind New Orleans piano virtuoso Marcus Roberts play Maple Leaf Rag, I see his right hand embark on bold leaps in register while his left hand strides from the low end of the instrument to the middle range on every beat. Wherever this uncanny ability to find the right notes without looking comes from, it isn't evident to my eyes.

It is easy to say that Ray, Stevie, and Art "play by ear", but that is an unsatisfying answer; of course they can hear what the next note should be, as can almost anyone who is capable of singing. The ear can hear where the right notes should be, but finding them without looking is like a shot in the proverbial dark.

There is another way to aim. We all possess an invisible secret sense that is under-appreciated and not consciously present. In 1906 the English neurophysiologist CS Sherrington coined the term "proprioception", from proprio- (one's own) and

-capio (to grasp), to describe this sixth sense of body position and movement. Some of his patients with proprioceptive deficits were unable to keep track of where their body parts were without looking; a person's arm might float up away from the body aimlessly without the owner being aware of it. When the patient saw that the limb was out of position they could voluntarily bring it back to their side, or to the table, or to touch their head, but as soon as they stopped watching the errant body part it would again drift off as if detached from the body.

As is often the case in brain studies, pathologic malfunctions reveal how our normal healthy bodies function in everyday life. Lifting a glass of water to our mouth without spilling would be impossible if not for Dr. Sherrington's "secret sense." Even a sober driver would be unable to walk the white line or touch his nose during a sobriety test without it. We need proprioception if we are to move smoothly through our world.

If a lack of proprioception takes away the ability to sense bodily position and movement, then perhaps a particularly well-developed sixth sense accounts for the amazing body control of a Michael Jordan, a Simone Biles, or an Arthur Rubinstein. Knowing where we are and in what direction we are moving is necessary if we are to arrive where we intend.

The mechanics of proprioception, although hidden mysteriously below our normal level of consciousness, are explainable. Mechano-sensory receptors are scattered throughout joints, tendons, and muscles, and they come in a variety of flavors; some provide information on the velocity of a moving body part, while others track the load on a limb or the stretching of a joint as it approaches its limit. This information travels to centers in the brain where the message is integrated with signals from the other senses and relayed to the motor cortex, allowing real-time adjustments to the muscle contractions that guide the desired movement. Of course, humans are not the only beings with proprioception; the leopard leaping from a tree to land squarely onto it's prey, the swallow banking to catch an insect, or the spider jumping to a distant branch to attach its web all use their own version of this sense of speed and direction Many of the amazing abilities of animals reveal that their proprioception (within their own realm) far exceeds our own humble abilities. Cats in particular seem to enjoy showing off their pinpoint bodily control as they leap up to a balcony railing, sticking the landing with feline nonchalance.

If proprioception is our secret sense for bodily control, it doesn't normally operate alone. Perhaps the reason that it is ignored is that it usually works with vision and balance, the Three Musketeers of Movement. If the trio should become a duo of proprioception and balance, we can still walk reasonably well. If our sense of proprioception should leave us, vision and balance can get us where we need to go. And if balance should become impaired, vision and proprioception can come to the rescue. But vision and balance take a back seat when it comes to music: Pianists can find their way without sight, and balance simply keeps the player from falling off the piano bench. Proprioception is clearly of prime importance.

The basic nature of music relies on proprioception, which is predictive, hinting at what is to come next and planning how we might get there. Even listening to and appreciating music comes from forward-moving expectations that may be dashed (tension) or arrived at (resolution). The primacy of motion is expressed by the very vocabulary of music: A melody moves in steps (whole or half) or leaps of varying intervals, even though there is no actual motion between the tones; they simply have different frequencies. Bach is famous for creating "forward motion" by slurring from an off-beat note to the next downbeat note to enhance the feeling of "falling forward", but there is no real movement involved. Even at the level of musical form the feeling of journeying through space is expressed in a symphony's "movements". We are always moving toward a destination, in music and life, trying to anticipate and reach for the next secure resting spot.

What are the possibilities of proprioception? Fats Waller and other great pianists of early jazz played a stride style with the their left hand dancing between bass notes and chords, making the leaps at least once a second and changing the notes each time while the right hand improvises syncopated 16th-note figures. In stride piano the left hand travels two feet back and forth, landing on precisely the right notes within an accuracy of 5mm, every time.

This large-scale positional navigation is impressive enough, but when proprioception is applied to stringed instruments the demands are even more impressive. I learned to play guitar using a pick, a thin piece of plastic held between my right thumb and forefinger with 2mm showing between the fingers. Occasionally I have had a minor cut on my thumb that required a Band-Aid to prevent blood on the strings, and even with the thinnest of adhesive strips my thumb hits the strings every time I try to pick a note. My sense of thumb position clearly functions at distances less than a millimeter.

When learning guitar this spacial ability developed on its own, with no conscious effort. But when I decided to learn to play the violin in my 70th year I found that the demands on my proprioception were even greater. As the violin bow glides across the second string, it misses the first and third strings by less than a millimeter; as a beginner, it is nearly impossible to maintain a sense of the bow in relation to each string, but it is painfully obvious to the ear when the bow brushes an adjacent string by accident. Since millions of people successfully play the violin, I have to assume that at some point the sense of bow proprioception will develop, but right now it eludes my abilities.

To make violin even more challenging, it isn't just the position of the hand and arm that the brain needs to monitor; two feet of bow serves as an extension to the hand, requiring that the player's proprioception extends out through the arm and into the springy wood and horsehair that contacts the strings. It has been shown that in people who regularly use a cane for walking the sensory body map in the brain comes to include the cane as if it were actually part of the hand and arm, a proprioceptive extender. Competent violinists likely have a similar cortical mapping of the bow's position and motion.

Given the proprioceptive demands that the violin requires, there is little room for error. Although joint flexibility helps generate the smooth swooping and gliding which gives bowed instruments their haunting human-voice-like qualities, too much laxity can be harmful. The sensors in the joints of the fingers, wrists, elbows, and shoulders are sensitive to the slightest change in position, but if the joint capsules are too stretchy the nerve endings may not register precise information. Rapid growth in young musicians sometimes makes it hard for them to clearly sense the position of the limbs. Young female violinists are particularly prone to Joint Hypermobility Syndrome, in which the flexibility of the joints interferes with accurate proprioceptive signals, severely hampering their ability to master the instrument.

Some teachers recommend muscle-strengthening exercises to limit the range-of-motion in the critical joints, but young players sometimes become discouraged and give up before their joints mature and proprioception improves.

The importance of proprioception to the musician seems self-evident, but the secret sense is involved in listening to and enjoying music as well. Academics argue about whether music or dance developed first in our ancestors, and likely they would need evidence from hominids much earlier than our current sapiens species to know. Shared human experience tells us that enjoying music is intimately associated with bodily motion; you need to move to groove.

When we describe the experience of music, it is evident that what seems like an auditory activity is closely linked to a sense of movement, even when the movement is not creating the music. Keiko Asakura studied the ability of non-musicians to learn to sing a new song and to describe the level of enjoyment that it produced. Some of the subjects learned the song while moving (not playing an instrument, but simply moving to the music), while others were stationary. The group that participated in bodily movement learned the song faster and reported more enjoyment. Music is movement. In addition, music therapists have used music to help develop proprioceptive ability in autistic and mentally challenged patients, finding that music helps connect the brain with the movement of the body. Perhaps highly proprioceptive activities like playing basketball should be accompanied by suitable music, which makes me wonder what type of music Michael Jordan listened to while he practiced his jump shot.

Can proprioception be developed? Musicians might find it helpful eliminate the visual input that we tend to rely upon. I have tried a donning a light-proof sleeping mask as I practiced music that required accurate movements, as when attempting to learn a ragtime piano piece. Did it help? Hard to tell; I suspect it would have taken more hours than I gave it. When I studied the upright double bass my left hand fingers would regularly become lost on the barren expanse of a fretless fingerboard two and a half feet long and my teacher would have me do "target practice", moving from the lowest position to some selected note farther up the string. My accuracy did improve gradually, especially if I didn't look at what I was doing.

In an attempt to determine how proprioception and hearing interact, researchers asked subjects move their hands to spots on the keyboard where specific notes were located without the aid of hearing the resulting pitch, in order to isolate proprioception from auditory input. The subjects were able to learn to hit the right notes with proprioception alone, although hearing the results helped.

My personal feeling is that proprioception can be developed, but we don't devote much practice time to developing the sense. It grows naturally in the learning of an instrument, but it might be that the development could be sped up if we challenged our proprioceptive system by blocking the sense of sight and deliberately asking the hands and arms to find their correct destination using the nervous system's own GPS. One of the prescriptions for pianists to improve their sight reading is to place an obstruction over the keyboard to prevent the student from seeing their hands.

But our secret sense has functions more profound than simply finding where the right notes are. In his quirky and arcane book, "Ways of the Hand", David Sudnow describes in agonizing detail his quest, not just to play jazz piano, but to become a jazz pianist. He studied and practiced long hours to learn the jazz chords and how to use his left hand to propel an improvisation. He mastered all of the scales and melodic figures needed to make his right hand journey convincingly in spontaneous improvisation over the left hand chords. After years of study he sounded "jazzy" and even played gigs regularly, but he felt something was missing; he didn't feel like he was "doing jazz". The feeling of jazz rising spontaneously from his pianistic perambulations never appeared.

David's epiphany occurred when he heard jazz pianist Jimmy Rowles play at a nightclub in Greenwich Village. He was struck by the way the legendary master addressed his instrument:

"Jimmy Rowles had a way with the instrument. He sat rather low down and stretched back, almost lazy with the piano, like a competent driver is nonchalant behind the wheel on an open road. ...
I watched him night after night, watched him move from chord to chord with a broadly swaying participation of his shoulders and entire torso, watched him delineate waves of movement, some undulating strokes with finer rotational movements, so that as his arm reached out to get from one chord to another it was as if some spot on his back, for example, circumscribed a small circle at the same time, as if at the very slow tempos this was a way a steadiness to the beat was sustained. ... As his foot tapped up and down, his head went through a similar rotational course, and the strict up-and-down tapping of the foot was incorporated within a cyclical manner of accenting his bodily movements. In an anchored heel, you could see only the up-and-down movements

of the foot, but in the accompanying head rotation and shoulder swaying, you could see a circularly undulating flow of motion, a pushing and releasing, a thrust and relaxation.... his observable bodily idiom, his style of articulating a beat, served as a guide. In the very act of swaying gently and with elongated movements through the course of playing a song, the lilting, stretching, almost oozing quality of his interpretations could be evoked."

When Sudnow imitated Rowles' distinctive movements at his own piano, he found that bits of real jazz appeared, surprising and fluent stretches of melody that seemed to play themselves. At first these glimpses would come and go, brief and unbidden, but with time his playing changed from "jazz-like" to the sort of spontaneous musicality toward which he had been striving. The magic seemed to be embodied in the postures and movements of his entire body. Motion became music.

I close my eyes as I sit on the stool in front of my living room piano, an 1862 rosewood Steinway upright. I reach for what I hope is middle C, then crack one eye just enough to see that my thumb is actually on E. Closing my eyes again, I move my right hand toward the E an octave higher, trying to gain a conscious feel for the how my arm and hand traverse seven inches to the right to land on the higher E. My ear tells me that I arrived at the correct note, so I recall my hand to the lower E, and then send it on a two octave leap to the next E above, landing on both the E and the D next to it.

Proprioception is there somewhere, I tell myself, but I still can't feel it. The secret sense awaits refinement, and I have to trust that this movement superpower lies just under the surface, waiting to be activated. I know where I want to go; I just need to close my eyes and make the leap.

5

ALL OVER THE MAP

Flawless technique, powerful stage presence, and striking blonde beauty made Liona Boyd one of the world's most sought-after classical guitarists from the early 1970s until 2002. The Canadian reigned as the "First Lady Of The Guitar", playing for world leaders and circling the globe in her concert career.

But shortly after the millennium Liona noticed a problem with the middle finger of her right hand. At first it simply didn't blend well with the adjacent fingers when she executed a tremolo, the classical guitar technique which uses the ring, middle, and index finger in rapid succession to create a floating repetition on a single note. With time the situation worsened, and her middle finger contracted disobediently toward her palm at the moments when it was most needed. Her career was put on hold as she tried everything to fix her fingers: the best neurologists, acupuncture, Alexander Technique, and even a witch doctor chanting and spitting on her to banish whatever evil spirits had tied up her hand.

Ms. Boyd did not have a hand problem; the malfunction was in her brain. The organization of the central nervous system is a powerful source of our ability to adapt, but adaptability brings its own problems.

Looking down at the surface of the brain, an observer might imagine a map of the body drawn in sensory and motor neurons arranged roughly in the shape of a person, with disproportionately larger areas devoted to the most important body parts. In 1951 Dr. Wilder Pennfield pioneered the mapping of the cerebral cortex, which involved a lot of poking patients' brains with electrodes under local anesthesia to determine what each area of the brain's surface does. He pictured the functional arrangement of neurons as a homunculus, a little man. Artists have translated Pennfield's picture into an image of a grotesque human form laying across the top of the brain, with shrunken legs and torso hanging into the chasm between the cerebral hemispheres and the upper body spread out across the top of the brain. The hands are magnified, demanding more brain "real estate" to facilitate their complex functions. The thumb is drawn the largest, but each finger claims its own distinct strip of tissue for feeling and movement. The head and face areas drape down the sides of the brain, claiming a disproportionate amount of brain space. The areas controlling the lips are grotesquely enlarged, the tongue even more so. The artist's rendering of Dr. Pennfield's map looks disturbingly like Mick Jagger.

But this map of brain functions is not etched permanently on the cortex. In the past two decades neurologists have coined the term "neuroplasticity" to describe the ability of the brain to change where things happen within the available nerve tissue. For example, if a person loses their right index finger in an accident, the brain will eventually allow the middle finger to access the unused index finger territory for its own purposes.

The principle of neuroplasticity is basic to the way the brain works. In a completely blind person the unused occipital cortex, where visual stimuli are turned into pictures, may gradually become the property of the auditory system, so that the processing of what the blind person hears occurs partly in the brain area normally dedicated to sight. Does that mean that a blind person is actually 'seeing' music as well as hearing it?

Neuroplasticity is central to our ability to learn a musical instrument. It has been shown that spending years of musical practice creates changes in the cortical brain map. In brass instrumentalists, the exaggerated representation of the lips on the cortical homunculus becomes even larger, like Mick Jagger with collagen enhancement. The brain claims whatever nerve cells are necessary to accomplish the tasks that are repeated most often.

The hands demand the most specialization in the nervous system, and this is reflected in the detailed brain map of thumbs and fingers. After years of guitar practice the outline of each finger on the left hand is expanded and defined on the surface of the right cerebral cortex. Classical guitarists spend countless hours developing the ability of each finger to operate independently when pressing strings against the guitar fingerboard; a brain surgeon with a stimulating electrode could likely tell whether a patient was a guitarist or not by tracing the distinct outlines of the four fingers of the left hand.

But things are different for the upright bassist. Bassists, whether jazz or orchestral, are trained to use only three sets of fingers: the index, middle, and combined ring finger and pinky. Using the ring and little fingers together provides more strength to depress the heavy strings of the bass, and the brain adjusts to this combined use. After years of practice the brain map of a bassist starts to fuse the areas of the third and fourth fingers as if they were a single digit.

For most people, bending the left little finger without also lowering the ring finger is difficult, but after thirty years of on-and-off guitar study I developed the ability to hold a complicated chord with fingers one, two, and three while pressing a different melody note with my littlest finger.

In my fifth decade, after an unsuccessful fling with the piano, I took up the upright bass. My bass teacher emphasized proper bass technique, and soon I was using my third and fourth fingers as if they were one. I could almost feel the brain map of my fingers starting to merge. When I did pick up a guitar again I found that some of my hard-won finger independence had faded. Eventually I realized that my brain couldn't have it both ways, fingers independent but also merged into a single entity.

The dark side of neuroplasticity is that the brain map isn't fixed permanently, even when we wish that it was. As neurons transfer their functions from place to place, mixups can occur, as if half of Connecticut slipped over into New York on the US map, sending an unlucky motorist to Buffalo rather than Hartford.

Liona Boyd's musical career came to a halt when her right hand fingers tightened and refused to straighten when she plucked the guitar strings. At first she thought she just needed rest from a grueling concert tour and she hid her condition from audiences, concert promoters, and even her agent. Eventually Ms. Boyd sought the help of a neurologist, who informed her somberly that she suffered a condition called Musician's Dystonia (MD), referred to as Focal Hand Dystonia in non-musical sufferers. Her prognosis was not encouraging; a number of performing careers have been interrupted, often permanently, when the musician's hands (or lips, in the case of horn players) inexplicably become uncooperative—but only during the specific tasks involved with music. During non-musical tasks the fingers act like nothing is wrong. Pianist Glen Gould;, the eccentric Bach interpreter of the mid-20th century, struggled with MD. Keith Emerson, of the progressive rock supergroup Emerson, Lake, and Palmer, was afflicted with the condition and plunged into depression and alcoholism, ultimately resorting to suicide. Jazz guitar prodigy Julian Lage was forced to stop playing for several years after relentless eight-to-ten hour days of practicing as a teenager led to dystonia. Julian's inability to control his left index and middle fingers first struck in the middle of a concert, forcing him to finish the gig by fretting with only his ring and little fingers. The problem seemed to go away, but the next year it returned unpredictably and kept him from performing for a year.

Famed classical pianist and Kennedy Center Honoree Leon Fleisher details his 30 year struggle with dystonia in his memoir, "My Nine Lives". Fleisher's right hand abandoned him, forcing him to perform music for the left hand only and diverting him into new careers in conducting and teaching. After years of therapy and botox injections in his right hand, he finally made a triumphant comeback, playing Mozart's Piano Concerto #12 with the Cleveland Orchestra.

Even non-musicians who depend upon detailed repetitive skills may be sidelined by dystonia; cartoonists Scott Adams (Dilbert) and Berkely Breathed (Bloom County) struggled when their artwork was disrupted by loss of control over their fingers while drawing.

The mutiny of the highly trained hand seems mysterious; this isn't an overuse syndrome where the joints and tendons complain from too much stress and strain. What these musicians all suffered from was literally "all in their head", the dark side of neuroplasticity.

The finely drawn neuronal representations that are sketched across the cerebral cortex can be smudged, resulting in confusion about which finger belongs where and an inability to straighten the fingers on command.

One way this occurs is when years of intense practice lays down a solid outline of each finger, and then a new practice routine (as when I changed from using my third and fourth fingers separately on guitar to using them together on bass) tries to change the brain's picture. (Fortunately, I have never practiced enough to develop a seriously confused brain map.) Musician's Dystonia also seems to be more common in musicians that double on multiple different instruments.

Most of the performers who have been struck by MD have been those who are legendary for obsessively long hours in the practice room. When the hand spends the majority of its time repeating the same precision movements, even asking the hands to do everyday sorts of things, like writing with a pen or eating with a fork, may create conflicting nerve signals, distorting the brain map and crossing the signals sent to the fingers. After decades have been devoted to their development, the hands are unsure what they are supposed to do. The afflicted musician wants to yell at the hands "How could you betray me like this?"

There are dozens of stories of recovery after months or years of retraining the brain, each with a different path to regaining control.. There are also scores of stories of hopelessness, performing careers that ended in teaching, composing, or delivering mail for a living.

Liona Boyd considers herself lucky. She tried all of the therapies that her doctor could conjure with only moderate improvement. Knowing that she could never regain concert-level skills, she watched a lifetime of music evaporate in her disobedient hands.

Ultimately she was saved by a resilient attitude: Accepting her musical disability, Liona discovered her voice. She veered into a career as a singer-songwriter. Her remaining guitar abilities are more than adequate for accompanying herself as she sings, and her set list still includes a few less-demanding classical pieces that she plays with imperfect technique, but with a greater appreciation for the beauty that can be drawn from the strings and fingers. The brain has resources that are not bounded by the movable map on its surface.

6

DIFFERENT STROKES

The room is buried in the Old Seattle Underground; in 1889 a great fire leveled the young city on the shores of Elliot Bay, and the hilly topography made rebuilding the old brick structures impossible. As a result, the streets were filled in up to the second floor of the buildings which surround the current Pioneer Square, and the second stories became the ground floors. In the 1960's historians discovered that the original catacomb-like first levels of the old buildings could be accessed by a steep stairway into the underground, and some of the rooms were excavated to provide cramped commercial spaces.

DeNunzio's Italian Restaurant was a tenant in one of these subterranean vaults, surrounded by old brick walls and the ghosts of Seattle pioneers. It was here that I learned to play upright bass in a trio with businessman and amateur pianist Jack Hunden and a promising young drummer named D'vonne. The trio played jazz every Friday and Saturday night; we weren't paid, but when we took a break after our first set the cooks would create something that wasn't on the menu for us to enjoy and we would relax with a glass of wine and a plate of delicious pasta before our second set.

One evening Jack's wife Pam came in to have dinner and listen to the trio, and her sister came along. As Jack and I joined them for our between-sets meal, Pam's sister asked a question that all jazz musicians hear frequently: "Where is the melody? I don't recognize anything that I can hum."

In all fairness, my own wife often makes the same complaint, so I'd had ample time to formulate an explanation of how listening to jazz differs from enjoying other instrumental music, such as classical.

"Listening to classical music is like looking at a great painting. You can stand before the Mona Lisa and enjoy the familiar image. You can contemplate how perfect the brushstrokes are, how the light is captured, and why her smile seems so enigmatic."

"But listening to jazz is more like sitting around a campfire, mesmerized by staring into the flames; every moment is new, a flicker of blue flame jumping up and disappearing instantly, the play of orange fire clinging to the side of a piece of pine, a spray of sparks as a chunk of wood collapses into the coals". None of these ephemeral moments are memorable or worthy of verbal description, yet you can't help but watch to see what comes next. Both the newness and the fleetingness keep us watching until the fire burns down to embers and we retire to our tent.

Metaphor can suggest different ways to listen, but our musical perceptions must be explained by brain function. This begs the question of how the experiences of classical music or jazz stimulate our nervous system in such different ways. And what about rock, pop, or country? Or Indian ragas, African chants, or Javan gamelan music?

My current exploration compares jazz and classical music; no insult is intended to Aerosmith or Garth Brooks, but jazz and classical are mostly instrumental music, eliminating the confounding effects of lyrics, and both require highly developed skills by the musicians who play them.

Forgive a brief digression into my philosophy of music appreciation and the relative worth (if there is such a thing) of different styles.

In most college courses, Music Appreciation classes concentrate on how to recognize the great works of the classical European composers. Nothing is mentioned about any music that involves guitars, drums, or electricity. A class in Popular Music or The History of Jazz might be offered, but those are likely to be social histories rather than explorations of the state of mind needed to enjoy each genre.

My view is that every musical style has elements that stay the same and elements that vary, and when a person says that they don't like a style of music it usually means that they are listening for the elements that vary in their favored brand of music and finding it lacking, or they expect to hear an unchanging element and feel that it is missing in a different style. They complain that Debussy's compositions just don't have a beat, or that the timbre of Bob Dylan's voice isn't pure and resonant. If I were to design a music listening curriculum, it would involve learning to identify and appreciate which qualities vary and which ones stay the same across the spectrum of musical genres. Open ears and an open mind.

For the sake of exploring the brain, I checked out some of the research on music perception and found several studies that compare jazz and classical music.

Neurologists, of course, are most interested in "the room where it happens"—the neural real estate where stimuli and responses can be measured with state-of-the-art electromagnetic imaging. It turns out that listening to and playing music involve a wide network of different structures, specialized for different musical features within the brain. Some (but not all) are shared by language, some are shared by body movement, and some are shared by hearing in general. How these centers interact is an interesting story.

In an article called "How Does the Brain Process Music?", from Clinical Medicine, February 2005, neurologist Jason Warren provides a full-page schematic diagram of the major connections involved in musical perception. Without reproducing the entire figure, a partial description illustrates the interconnectedness of the network: A musical sound enters the Primary Auditory Cortex and information is sent to the Planum Temporale (PT) to analyze the pitch, intervals, melody, timbre and spatial locations; simultaneously a message is sent to the Right Lateral Herschel's Gyrus (HG) to have a listen for pitch, interval and melody. The PT also relays the story to the Parietal Lobe (PL) for analysis of rhythm and the engagement of working memory, spatial location, and cross-modal sharing. The PT also refers it to the Medial Temporal Gyrus (MTG) for recognition and cross-modal associations. In the meantime, the HG sends its message to the Superior Temporal Gyrus (STG) to check out the pitch interval, meter, rhythm, timbre, and to check for recognition. From the STG the music is sent to the Temporal Pole for more recognition and cross-modal analysis, and input from the TP is joined by the PL and travels to the frontal lobe for evaluation of harmony, key, emotion, working memory, and behavioral output. Even this mind-numbing musical travelogue leaves out visits to the language areas, the emotional centers, and the motor circuits that make us want to dance and play air guitar. Suffice it to say that musical functions are modular and very widely distributed in the nervous system, which is why some musical abilities are pre-served, even in strokes or dementia.

If we presume that every type of music generates its own network among the music centers and connects the most fre-quently used areas, this gives laboratory researchers (admittedly not "real world" music experience) an opportunity to scan the brain while hearing or playing music to find out what goes on inside.

Although listening to different genres of music produces different processing patterns. the effects are more clear when the subjects are experienced musicians. One common study strategy is to create musical sequences that contain unexpected chords, out-of-tune notes, timbre mis-matches (such as a flute segment in a piano melody), rhythmic hiccups, or unexpected jumps of melody. The recordings are played to musicians while they un-dergo brain imaging and the degree to which the different mod-ules in the brain light up measures each area's involvement. A brief survey reveals several interesting findings.

One study compared jazz, classical, and rock musicians, and found that classical players were more sensitive to tuning and timing, rock musicians lit up more in melodic contour cen-ters, and jazz musicians showed stimulation of the areas involved in timing, melodic contour, and transposition, as well as auditory changes of any kind.

Another study asked jazz and classical musicians and non-musicians to listen to a bebop jazz improvisation by Charlie Parker and rate the "expectedness" of each note—did the melody proceed in a logical manner? Musicians were more sensitive to orderliness of the melody than non-musicians, and as expected, jazz musicians were the most tuned in to any surprising notes. It was noted that the classical musicians recognized the unexpected notes implicitly, knowing intuitively that the notes sounded out of place, while jazz musicians heard the same notes explicitly, and were able to give computational estimates—a melody that might have gone up by an interval of a fifth jumped instead by a flatted fifth, and the contrast was consciously noted.

In order to quantify the gap between jazz and classical, pianists were shown the same sequence of melody on a computer-graphics keyboard display and asked to imagine that they were playing the music. When a "wrong" chord or melody note was shown, the musicians had to adjust as they would to play the out-of-place sequence. Jazz pianists started planning where the music was going in .4 seconds, while classical players took .6 seconds. Pianists who were expert in improvising could rapidly adjust to a strange harmony, but classical players figured out the fingering that would be required and made less mistakes. Jazz players concentrated on the "what", while classical musicians were more concerned with "how", making use of different musical modules in different parts of the brain.

On the whole, jazz musicians were better at hearing melody and harmony as they played, and were less concerned about the fingering, tone, and timbre. Classical players devoted more attention to the details, perfect notes played perfectly.

It isn't surprising that different styles of music draw on different parts of the brain, but rarely are the skills separated completely. In actuality, most modern jazz musicians also have classical training, and even the most traditionally taught classical musicians have at least dabbled in improvised music. The resumes of many rock musicians reveal other musical worlds.

Drummer Charlie Watts of the Rolling Stones considers his studies in jazz as an essential part of his approach, and jazz pianist Kenny Kirkland had toured with the Stones regularly. Some of the most iconic jazz musicians were classically trained, including Herbie Hancock, Ron Carter, and Wynton Marsalis. The first two of these were discouraged from following classical music careers because as African Americans they would never be hired by any major orchestra. The brain wiring of these musicians must be complicated, but it still maintains the modular organization in which different elements of the music live in separate areas.

Pianist Keith Jarret lived in both worlds (until a stroke in 2018 left him unable to play and forced his retirement); he is widely recognized as the consummate spontaneous improvisor, and his music embodies in-the-moment composition, rarely resorting to practiced melodic patterns or cliched licks. In 1975 he recorded a solo concert in Cologne, Germany that made history. The music was completely improvised on the spot, under the most difficult of conditions, and the backstory is part of jazz legend.

The concert at the Cologne Opera House had been arranged by Vera Brandes, a 17-year-old pianist and aspiring promoter, but everything fell into chaos. Although a world-class Bosendorfer grand piano had been arranged for the performance, what was mistakenly delivered to the concert stage was an old practice piano, out of tune and in poor physical shape; some of the keys and pedals didn't even work. Jarrett, who is a famously temperamental perfectionist, cancelled the performance when he discovered what he was being asked to play. In addition, he was sleep-deprived from a brutal European touring schedule and in severe back pain. He insisted that the concert be called off, but as he sat in the car waiting for a ride back to his hotel, Ms. Brandes, rain-soaked and desperate, tapped on his car window and begged and pleaded for him to perform the show, despite the conditions.

Jarrett must have recognized her passion for the music and he relented. The opera house was filled to capacity, 1400 people who were willing to take whatever music the pianist could muster. What they witnessed was a masterpiece of continuous improvisation that touched on modern jazz, classical, folk, gospel, and latin influences, avoiding the keys that didn't work and mixing the weak bass register with the tinny high notes to create magic. Fortunately, Jarrett's record producer recorded the evening, immortalizing The Koln Concert as the pinnacle of the jazz art, and the best selling jazz piano record of all time.

Keith Jarrett is also a world-class classical pianist and composer, with a long list of classical recordings and prestigious prizes to his credit. An interviewer once asked if he would consider someday performing a concert in which he would play both jazz and classical pieces. Jarrett laughed incredulously and replied, "No, that's hilarious…It's like a chosen practically impossible thing…(because of) the circuitry. Your system demands different circuitry for either of those things."

Jarrett knew intuitively what brain imaging studies have confirmed: Music requires a variety of neurologic functions, and different types of music draw on different combinations of these abilities. But perhaps the magic of The Koln Concert was that the chaotic situation created an all-hands-on-deck, fight-or-flight synergy that called on his complete array of musical resources, music without borders. The brain may be made up of many different parts, but they are expressed through a single consciousness.

7

HAVING A MOMENT

I will always remember my first time. It was my freshman year of college and I had joined the WSU Stage Band, practicing every Wednesday evening in the basement of the Kimbrough Music Building. I was not a music major, so I didn't qualify to play in the "A" band; I was relegated to the "B" band, which was full of engineering and chemistry majors and in need of a guitarist. The university was not a center of jazz hipness even for the music majors, who were mostly average classical players destined to become music teachers. What I remember was just a rehearsal, but it was one of the most significant musical experiences of my life.

We were running through an up-tempo Charlie Parker composition called "Dewey Square" (named after a landmark in Boston, with maybe a subtle dig at Parker's new young trumpeter, Dewey Miles Davis), and there was nothing special about the tune. The director, trombonist Michael O, was no hipper than the students who made up the band, and he had the annoying habit of stopping the music every few bars to correct some minor detail. But this time was different: Fifteen seconds in, the music felt different. I could sense that the other players in the band knew it too; we held our breath for a few moments, waiting for Mr. O to wave us to a stop, but the expected interruption never came and the music gathered momentum, with boppish trumpet lines blazing over angular chords from the sax section. Back in the rhythm section, I felt like I was in perfect synch with the piano, bass, and drums, pushing the horns as they cruised through the head of the song. Second trumpet Jim O'Bannion, a pre-med major, stood to take a solo over the riffing horns, and we all felt it; he had never played so forcefully, effortlessly spinning lines that any professional would have been pleased with. We dived back into the recapitulation of the tune without losing a step, and I noticed that Mr. O had abandoned any pretense of conducting the band. His hands were clenched at his side and his foot was tapping uncontrollably. The piece finished with the lead trumpet's last note hanging over the band's final chord by a perfect fraction of a second. Nobody moved for a full half minute as we sat in awed silence. There was no need for anyone to voice the obvious: "What just happened?" It seemed like the music had played itself, and the separation between our individual parts had melted away in the torrent of music. Could this be what music was supposed to feel like?

It was twenty years later that this feeling earned a name in the psychology of optimal performance: Flow.

Psychologist Mihaly Csikszentmihalyi had spent two decades studying what made people happy, and he had found that fame, fortune, and sex just didn't do it. In fact, perhaps "happiness" wasn't exactly the best word for the feeling of fulfillment and meaning that people in all cultures seek above all else. "People typically feel strong, alert, in effortless control, unselfconscious, and at the peak of their abilities" when they are completely absorbed in an activity, whether it is music, sports, or coding computer programs. "Both a sense of time and emotional problems seem to disappear, and there is an exhilarating feeling of transcendence". In 1990 Mihaly shared his research and ideas in a ground-breaking book, "Flow: The Psychology of Optimal Experience".

Characteristics of the flow experience are remarkably similar across divergent activities, and always involve both skill and challenge. The feeling arises when a difficult task is met with a skill level that is just barely up to the task. The concentration involved requires complete focus, but is accompanied by a feeling of control that is often missing in our normal lives. The experience may not always be pleasant during the event (swimming the English Channel through icy water, for instance), but the feeling of euphoria that comes from meeting the challenge is addictive.

Flow has been identified as both a state (the feeling surrounding an activity) and as a trait (a personality characteristic that makes it easier to enter the flow state). Mihaly uses the term "autotelic" to suggest that the activity is done simply for the reward of having done it, not because it earns the participant money or glory. The feeling comes from having a goal that balances ability and difficulty.

A downhill ski racer may experience flow during a great run down a difficult course, but the average skier may feel the same rush when making their way down an easy slope that is just at the edge of his or her ability. Everyone would like to share this feeling, but it isn't easy; it requires a delicate balance between challenge and skill level. A professional skier who has skied a dangerous black-diamond slope confidently a hundred times may not find it demanding enough to generate a thrill, while the beginner who has just enough skill to move from the beginner's slope to a rolling downhill may experience the perfect merging of skill and challenge.

Playing music offers just as many opportunities to crash and burn as skiing but with less risk, making it a favorite subject for studying flow. The critical ingredient is the balance between task and skill; from a physiologic perspective, the autotelic individual can find "the zone" by balancing the stimulation of the sympathetic (fight-or-flight) nervous system with the parasympathetic (rest-and-control) system. When this balance is achieved, the activity seems to become spontaneous and automatic; musicians who enter the flow state report that it is as if they are not thinking, but simply watching their hands play on their own. Time slows down, and it may seem like no time at all has elapsed. Consciousness of the individual self becomes less important, absorbing into the act itself.

Even though the psychological description of flow is modern, it is easily recognizable in the descriptions of many famous classical composers. Beethoven was notorious for becoming so focused on his composing that he would forget to eat, sleep, or attend to his personal needs. It doesn't require a psychologist to tell us that he was in a constant state of flow.

But it isn't easy for most of us. My first experience of losing myself in group musical activity made me hungry to relive the moment, but that was the only time that the B Stage Band ever hit that high note, in rehearsal or in performance. I don't remember moments like that when playing gigs with an R&B band to help pay for college schooling, or when directing a contemporary church choir for 10 years. I was competent enough at each that my skill was sufficient but the challenges provided by the relatively simple music were not demanding enough. During my later attempt to learn jazz piano, I never developed enough skill to feel like I had any level of control, even when playing in a casual evening class for novice jazz players.

After giving up piano I took up playing jazz bass; the competency bar for bass players is much more modest than for piano and I had ample playing opportunities to challenge my ability while using the basic skills that I had learned. The experiences that made me want to play music were occasional at best, and unpredictable, but there were moments.

My most memorable occasions occurred while playing in a trio with an excellent amateur pianist and a budding young professional drummer. We played regularly in a tiny basement Italian restaurant where there was no pressure to impress anyone; we were mostly ignored by the patrons and we weren't being paid. But there were moments. Occasionally I could tell what the pianist was going to play just as he played it and throw in off-beat accents to match his. When the drummer heard a hint of double-time tempo from the pianist, we would both sense it and run with it (and even if the pianist didn't intend to double the tempo the drummer and I would feel the energy and drag him along with us). These occurrences of musical synchronicity and creative fire might only last half a minute, but they were memorable. As we packed up at the end of the evening, we would nod and say "We had a few moments tonight". That was enough to make us look forward to the next Friday night.

It would be even better if those moments were easier to conjure up, going with the flow for longer than a few minutes at a time, but that is like trying to summon a lightening strike. Searching for a clue, I re-read pianist Kenny Werner's book, "Effortless Mastery: Liberating the Master Musician Within". Werner's credentials are impressive, having recorded with dozens of jazz masters, including Charles Mingus, Joe Lovano, Dave Holland, Jack DeJohnette, and the Thad Jones Orchestra. He also teaches seminars on finding what he calls "the space" from which music or other activity flows easily. The basics of Werner's philosophy are to stop worrying about impressing others, accept whatever comes out ("every note you play is the most beautiful sound in the world"), and don't think too hard. Oh, and practice enough to be prepared—but practice from "the space".

Werner describes his own "aha" moment when he was struggling with his own playing after lackluster stints at The Manhattan School of Music and Berklee School of Music, facing fear of failure and his own inadequacies. At the direction of a new teacher he stopped playing altogether, limiting his practice to five minutes a day of simply dropping each finger on a piano key repeatedly. After a period of time off he attended a party where the host asked him to play something; he tried to beg off, insisting that he had stopped playing and apologizing in advance. With no expectations and a mind cleared by his musical inactivity, he sat down and started to play Autumn Leaves. The notes flowed effortlessly, beautiful strands of melody and harmony that seemed to come from somewhere outside of himself. After what seemed like an eternity in a moment, he finished, dumbfounded. He suddenly understood that it had been his fears and need to impress that had stood between him and the music. His revelation led him to search the ancient spiritual traditions, where he found new ways of looking at the world and his music: Leaving ego behind, playing without fear, accepting and loving whatever came out, and allowing his consciousness to merge with that of his bandmates and the world at large. Zen and the Art of Music.

This search for higher consciousness is found in many of the great musicians. Herbie Hancock, Wayne Shorter, and Carlos Santana are among those who meditate, chant, and seek to play from a space of transcendent selflessness.

John Coltrane was most admired, not only for his legendary practice routines and virtuosic "sheets of sound", but for his spiritual quest to explore every possibility of the saxophone.

Elvin Jones, the drummer who propelled Coltrane's quartet during the 1960's, told of one memorable performance that started with a simple theme which led to an extended improvisation that lasted over three hours. 'Trane's ferocious intensity was matched by Jones' polyrhythmic drumming, Jimmy Garrison's guttural bass, and McCoy Tyner's storm of modal chords. One would expect that the musicians would have been drained and exhausted by the time the music faded, but when Jones was asked how he was able to summon enough stamina for the gale-force marathon, he replied that it seemed like no time had gone by, that the music had taken over and he was simply along for the ride. This anecdote reveals the power of flow, playing from the space, and being in the zone. But for for those of us who live ordinary lives there are also moments when the experience of flow can be felt.

Henry David Thoreau is remembered for many things: Naturalist, philosopher, contrarian writer, political protestor. But if asked, Henry would say that his most important activity was walking. At least four hours of every day must be spent sauntering in the woods and meadows, he insisted, and more if possible. Reading his biography, it is apparent that he constantly sought a state of flow in the woods, savoring every moment, disappointed when he lost contact with the feeling: "I am alarmed when I have walked a mile into the woods bodily, without getting there in spirit". If this was flow, where was the challenge needed to balance his skill as a woodsman? It lay in the task he set for himself to notice everything around him: The spacing of the oaks and pines, the resting spot of a ground-nesting bird, the berries that would ripen in a fortnight. Walking a familiar path was never the same from day to day and a different story was always waiting to be read. Henry was also well-known for playing his flute at all hours (Louisa May Alcott's elegiac poem, The Flute, takes the form of Henry's bereaved flute hanging from a tree until a breeze brings forth an ode to its master). I think I would have liked to walk with Henry, listen to him play his flute, and share a moment.

8

THE DAWN CHORUS

The first Sunday in May has been officially designated as International Dawn Chorus Day. People around the world are encouraged to get up early and go outside to drink in the sounds of the bird songs that erupt for a half-hour before and after sunrise.

The melodies produced in profusion by sparrows, wrens, thrushes, and starlings provide inspiration and joy, a fact that has not gone unnoticed by the great composers. It is said that Beethoven was inspired by the sounds of nature that infused his daily walks in the country. Birdsong surrounded him, and he jotted the songs of the cuckoo, the quail, and the nightingale in his pocket notebook, where they eventually found their way into his Pastorale Symphony and other works.

Mozart fashioned the final motif of his 17th piano concerto from the song of a cherished pet starling that he bought in 1784 in a Viennese pet shop. The theme did require a slight adjustment, lowering a G sharp to G natural to satisfy the musical ear of the time, but it is recognizable all the same. Similar relationships to bird song are found the music of Villa Lobos (Uirapuru), Oliver Messianen (Le Merle Noir), and Antonio Carlos Jobim (Passarin). It seems that human and avian music must share a close relationship, but there are those who claim that the similarities are superficial—that avian music is simply an "instinctive reflex" whose functions are strictly to warn of danger, to establish territory and attract mates, while human music is intended for emotional expression, spiritual uplift, and well, to attract mates.

Let's imagine a psychological experiment to investigate the utility and meaning of music. First, we would choose a group of people, let's say college sophomores (the usual psychology test subjects). Video recordings would be made of the twenty-year-olds in a closed room to establish a baseline. Then the subjects would be exposed to twenty minutes of classical music (Bach's First Solo Cello Suite would be an excellent choice) to see what difference the music made in the person's observable behavior. After a number of trials were made, the entire experiment would be repeated with heavy metal music, ACDC's Back in Black should do. Now compare the results. Did the students show different behaviors between the control condition, the classical condition, and the metal condition? What do the behaviors tell us about the meaning of music to these individuals? To go further, the experiment could be repeated in a natural environment, with the students wandering around loose on campus. We could then extend our investigation by asking students how they felt and what their inner thoughts and emotions were in order to find the meaning of music.

Now imagine that our research subjects are not college students, but songbirds. These are roughly the methods that scientists use to investigate how birds use their songs, but unlike the college student experiment, researchers can't ask the birds how they feel, but they can dissect the unfortunate birds' brains to find out what traces have been left by the songs that they produce. We can only guess at what we might discover in the brain cells of YoYo Ma, Charlie Parker, or Mick Jagger.

Philosophers, linguists, and musicologists might argue over whether bird song is "music" in the human sense, but intriguing insights have emerged from the scientific studies of feathery vocalizations.

The study of avian music surged in the late 1980's when it was discovered that new brain cells devoted to song could be formed, even in adult birds. One of the core beliefs of brain science had been that all of the neurons in the brain are added during the animal's growth period and after that brain cells could be lost, but new neurons could not be produced. In 1989 Professor Fernando Nottebohm at Rockefeller University's Field Research Center for Ethology discovered that the bird brain loses many of the cells that generate avian chirps and whistles during the winter dormant period. But in the spring, urged by a surge of testosterone, new nerve cells sprout and follow the supporting cells of the nervous system until they reach the song centers. Once the cells re-connect, the ability to sing the complex songs that declare territory and impress the local females is restored.

The implications of growing new brain cells immediately caught the attention of human neurologists, who longed for some secret process that would allow stroke or trauma patients to recover lost brain cells. Once it was shown that the adult brain has the latent ability to produce new cells, research money flowed into exploring "birdsong neurogenesis". Whether neurogenesis actually happens in people isn't as important as the suggestion that it could, but there has since been limited evidence of new cells being added to the adult human brain. Sadly, it has not been shown that the human brain can sprout new neurons that give us the ability to sing La Traviata or Carmen.

The location of song neurons is easier to trace in birds than in humans, where musical functions are more widely dispersed and mixed with movement and cognition. The brain areas described in bird brains are not the same areas used by people, but there is a lot to learned by comparison. The researchers at Rockefeller University studied canaries, because it was already known that two areas of the brain, the Higher Vocal Center (HVC) and the Robustus Archistraitalis (RA), were smaller during the winter and twice as large in the summer, which matched the seasonal song cycle.

To show that the growth of the HVC and RA was due to new neurons, they injected the birds with radioactive thymidine during the springtime before singing started; thymidine is one of the "letters" in the cell's DNA, so when the birds' brains were examined weeks later only the newly formed cells were radioactive. They found that for each day of treatment, 1% of the cells in the song centers were freshly minted. In addition, it was discovered that old neurons were disappearing as the new cells moved in.

Naturally, Nottenbohm and his crew had more questions. Why did only males sing? And why did females, that normally don't sing, also show seasonal increases in the song centers? They were also curious about how the new cells found their way to connect the brain areas.

Testosterone was the obvious answer to the first question: male hormone levels fluctuate seasonally, and correlate with singing activity. When males were injected with testosterone in the winter, they started singing and new nerve cells made their appearance. Even females started singing when given the male hormone. Strangely, even untreated females would show new cells in the HVC during the breeding season; apparently the song center is also critical for song recognition, and females also needed to increase their "music appreciation", or the males would just be singing for themselves.

Re-learning to sing every year has its advantages. When the winter-diminished HVC first starts to develop in the spring, canaries can change their songs, updating their repertoire for the upcoming breeding season. And the girls like the variety. But once the testosterone surge is in full swing the males stop experimenting and their songs become stereotyped.

Not all birds show seasonal growth of new cells for song. The scientists may have been lucky in their choice of canaries, as zebra finches (another bird commonly used for song studies) do not have changes in their HVC or RA, and they are unable to learn new songs in adulthood. Often luck plays a part in important discoveries.

The discovery of adult neurogenesis has sparked continued interest in birds' brains and song. The final word of the researchers at Rockefeller was that "adult brains possess considerable potential for self-repair of aged neurons".

AMAZING FACTS ABOUT BIRDSONG

Research interest in bird song has revealed a lot of intriguing facts and observations about avian vocalization. Let's take a break from the brain and listen to what birds can do:

The American Redstart sings one song during courtship, and then once a nest is built they sing a different tune (which might be said of many marriages).

During the day Eastern Towhees sing one of 3 to 8 different versions of "drink your tea" repeatedly, then switch to another version until after an hour they have gone through all their variations. At dawn, they sing directly through their entire repertoire all at once, in less than a minute

Chipping Sparrows have only one song (your basic "one hit wonder"), Song Sparrows have eight to ten songs, Marsh Wrens have more than a hundred on their playlist, and Mockingbirds alternate several hundred tunes. One Brown Thrasher showed off with more than two thousand different songs.

Black-capped Chickadees sing a simple "fee-bee-ee", but after two or three dozen repetitions they change to a higher or lower frequency. Most birds don't recognize their own songs if they are played back to them in a different key, so it isn't clear whether this sounds like a new melody, an easy way to add to their repertoire.

Male Stripe-back Wrens learn their father's song, but females learn their mother's.

If a White-Crowned Sparrow's song is interrupted by noisy parrots in the middle of a phrase, it will pick the song back up from where it left off, as we might continue with "as I was saying..."

In most birds from temperate climates only the male sings, but in the tropics both sexes often create intricate songs. One explanation is that sharing song helps the pair keep track of each other in the dense foliage.

Now back to the brain.

Birds are not hatched from the egg knowing how to sing, any more than humans come from the womb knowing three guitar chords. Since the song centers in the brain are a subject of scientific interest, this seems a good place to to start considering how birds learn their songs.

Like humans, young birds learn their basic vocabulary of sounds from their parents when they are young. As in children, there is a critical period when the developing brain is capable of distinguishing one syllable from another. This usually takes place in the first 70 days, and rarely can an entirely new chirp or whistle be learned later. Initially birds have the capacity to reproduce nearly any sound, but as they mature they discard the cells that encode the sounds that they won't use in adulthood. This is similar to the way that children who grow up hearing only the Japanese language will lose the ability to distinguish the L and R sounds in adulthood because the difference is not significant in the language that they are "imprinted" on. Avian researchers probably find it amusing when they raise fledgling cowbirds with canary foster parents and the cowbirds learn the canary sounds. As adults, these birds socialize and sing with canaries. But when a normal wild cowbird is put into the aviary, the fostered cowbirds are confused, since they can't make the sounds of their species. The young males end up performing their canary songs with each other, rather than engaging the stranger who looks like them but makes cowbird noises. This type of study has been repeated with many different species and with recorded bird calls that have been altered to see how the birds react. I imagine the Bach boys if they had grown up hearing only Led Zeppelin or Indian ragas; the music they wrote would have certainly sounded different and would have confused their German audiences.

Individual sounds are only a part of learning to sing. The way in which the syllables are strung together matters. In human language (and music) the order of the words or motifs creates a richness of meaning beyond the elements themselves, and bird song is constructed in a similar fashion. At first young birds just babble, chattering with rough approximations of the sounds they have heard. Soon syntactic patterns emerge: a young White-crowned Song Sparrow that is learning the ABCD song of the adult will first pair the A and B sounds, then the C and D sounds, before joining them in the entire phrase.

The brain of the songbird has specialized areas for learning song that are separate from producing the finished melody. This is the neural equivalent of having one place to learn the scales and exercises with which the human musician develops their skills and a separate area for performing a learned arrangement of Yesterday. Avian song is learned in an area called the Magnocellular nucleus of the Anterior Neostriatum (MAN); after learning the songs of its species the MAN shrinks by 50%, and the song is turned over to the Ventral Striatum (VS), which increases by a corresponding amount, the first indication that one brain area can increase at the expense of another area. The cells of the MAN don't just go away on their own: they become unable to eliminate testosterone and become drunk on male hormone until they are eliminated. Once testosterone has hardwired the final version of the song, the performance centers in the VS take over and song pours forth.

It is said that the main function of a music teacher is to tell the student what they are doing wrong. Birds have a separate brain area for that: the Ventral Tegmental Area (VTA) proofs the song and tells the bird when it deviates from the official version of the melody. But a nearby section called the Basal Ganglia

(BG) actively creates variations and adds them to the song, giving the VTA fresh material to reject or accept; mistakes are a part of learning. What good is trial-and-error if there are no errors?

Learning the sounds and the grammar happen together, in much the same way that language is learned in children. The linguist Noam Chomsky has suggested that people are naturally endowed with universal grammar, a tendency to seek patterns and organize vocalizations while they learn the words. Chomsky held that this "computational core of human language" was unique to people, but less human-centered researchers see the same tendency in some birds and other animals.

In cross-species studies, it appears that the individual sounds are learned from experience, but there is a rhythmical template that is born into the species, as if a person used Portuguese words within a Mandarin Chinese rhythm and structure.

Japanese Great Tits have several distinctive short tunes that they learn. The sequence ABC means "come over here", as when a tasty food source has been found. When they sing D, it means danger, as with a hawk circling overhead, and by itself it will signal other birds to shelter in place. However, if they sing ABC-D, nearby birds will quickly flock together to confront the danger and attack the predator. But when researchers altered recordings of the songs and played D-ABC, the birds ignored the danger message, paying as more attention to the order of sounds than to the sounds themselves.

Even more sophisticated grammatical constructions have been found in European Starlings. Some of their songs include a modifying phrase inserted into the middle of a longer sequence which adds meaning without interfering with the primary message of the song. This is a construction that Chomsky would term recursive, center-embedded grammar. Order brings meaning.

While interesting, all of this singing still seems a little automatic; unless science interferes, sparrow still sing just like sparrows. Do they sing instinctively with the sounds they have learned?

Even within populations of the same species, there are variations and dialects that are identifiable, even to human ears. Birds can distinguish others of their species that have a slightly different "accent"; even though the basic song is the same, they will chase away an intruder if it sings it differently from the normal residents of the neighborhood. But sometimes a novel take on an old song is taken up as the "new thing". The traditional White-throated Sparrow song ends in a triplet, and the birds had been singing it that way for years. In 2000, however, some of the birds in Western Canada started to shorten the three-note ending to two notes. The variation went viral, and by 2007 half of the sparrows in eastern Quebec and Vermont had adopted it as their own.

Sometimes a change in tune is due to the bird's environment: When Bluebirds sing amid urban noise they increase their volume and drop the frequency to a lower pitch to avoid high-pitched human sounds.

As birds are learning to sing, their warbles are full of overtones. While the extra vibrations that occur at two, three, or four times the fundamental frequency give the violin its rich voice and the distortion-laden rock guitar its growl, most birds prefer pure tones. It takes lots of practice to eliminate the overtones, evidence that an aesthetic sense is at work.

Audience reaction also helps influence how a bird sings. The Common Potoo sings a song based on the major pentatonic scale (C, D, E, G, A). If the females are not responding, however, the Potoo has a few tricks to wow his audience. First it will change the number of times a phrase is repeated. Not getting any love? Then the bird will raise the 6th of the scale (A) to a bluesy flat-7 (Bb). What girl could resist the passion of the flat-7?

There are also physical reasons why one bird's voice differs from another. Female cardinals learn the same songs as the males of the species, but their voices sound a little different, more nasal and full of harmonic overtones. Researchers suspect that hormones make the difference. Is that why Madonna sounds different from Springsteen?

"Where there is beauty, there is craft", states violin bow-maker Jeff Van Fosse. The fact that birds work at refining their song-making suggests that they strive to improve their performance to make it more beautiful. The reasons behind these efforts are many. If you want to impress and intimidate the neighbors, you can sing their songs right back at them: Marsh Wrens have 150 different songs, but if a nearby bird sings a particular tune, the neighbor quickly sings the same song, an avian version of trash-talking, "I can do that too—I know the whole songbook!".

Refining a duet between a male and a female can serve both to bond the pair and to warn other birds away, as if to say "Watch out, we've got each other's back". Singing duets is also useful to keep track of your mate in the dense tropical jungle. Bay Wrens duet with a WHOP-DIDDLY WHOP-DIDDLY call, one sex singing the WHOPs and the other the DIDDLYs. The brains of a duet-singing pair of birds change and synchronize, until the two brains are essentially functioning as one. Bonding over song.

Jazz musicians often "trade fours" after each soloist has had a chance to play their own solo. The tenor sax improvises a four bar melody, and then the trumpet comes in to imitate it, altering it to fit the harmony of the chord changes. Sometimes they trade two bar phrases, and occasionally they will play rapid-fire one-bar bursts. But these displays of human virtuosity are dwarfed by the Plain-tailed Wrens from Ecuador. They produce a duet in a pattern of ABCDABCD, with the male singing A and C and the female responding B and D. Each phrase comes in 20 or 30 different versions, each with 20 or 30 corresponding responses. The male sings one of his versions of A, the female responds with the matching B, the male sings one of his C options, and again the female chooses her appropriate D. And the entire sequence is repeated twice every second. Even more incredibly, another pair will join in, matching tune versions and responses so perfectly that when one bird drops out it isn't noticeable. The purpose of this virtuosic performance isn't clear, but it stretches the idea of what is musically possible.

Tracing avian music through the brain as it adds neurons, learns the song of its species, refines the performance, and joins or competes with other singers explains the bird's repertoire and technique, but we still wonder about why they sing. Some of the answers are obvious: Territory and mates. Songs are used to claim real estate and hold it by demonstrating the fitness and talents of the resident. Status can be established by the skill of the singer, and trading songs in a common dialect promotes tolerance between neighbors.

Love songs are important, to birds as well as people. Mates are attracted and pair bonding is maintained by a profusion of melody. Female Warblers in Sweden are attracted to mates with large repertoires and will indulge in "extra-pair copulation" (cheating) if another male has a bigger playlist than their mate. Having better music (and more testosterone) are powerful attractants.

There must be deeper meaning and motivation to the dawn chorus, when songbirds express themselves in response to the return of daylight. Is music a form of language, or is it more similar to human music? Birdsong is certainly used to communicate important information: Calling the flock to roost, warning of predators, drawing territorial boundaries. Like human language, song is produced by very specific centers of the avian brain. The grammatical structure of birdsong, syllables arranged in meaningful combinations, suggests a kinship to language.

But most people would agree that music is more than just communication. Birds strive to refine their songs to make them more precise, more varied, and yes, more beautiful.

Biologists suggest that the feeling of beauty is nature's way of motivating an organism to fulfill its needs; humans are filled with joy at the sight of a landscape that is verdant and fruitful, promising a good life, and it is reasonable to assume that other conscious organisms share the feeling. We can never know how it feels to be a bird, but naturalists know that birds will sing, even when it isn't breeding season, territory doesn't need to be defended, and the bird is well fed and stress free. Ornithologists intuitively understand that birds often vocalize because they are happy and it feels good to sing.

The feelings expressed by the singers may not be the same as the feelings of the human listeners, but we share a need for beauty and the expression of vitality, desire, togetherness, and for telling the universe that we are alive.

9

COLOR TONES

Gary is a pediatrician, but also an excellent musician with whom I play music occasionally. He has an unnerving ability to hear and automatically identify any pitch played by other members of our band, without even thinking about it. Gary has "perfect pitch", which seems like a musical super-power; but Gary plays drums, making his special ability less than useful. When he comments about a note or chord that the pianist or saxophonist plays, I am tempted to remind him, "Gary you're a drummer. Just hit something and leave the notes to us."

Gary is one of the one-in-ten-thousand people who have perfect pitch (more accurately termed "absolute pitch"). The name of every note he hears is immediately obvious to him, without effort or practice.

With intensive training many musicians can train themselves to have "relative pitch", the ability to identify a note by comparing it with tones that are already known. If middle C is played, relative pitch can suggest that the tone four steps higher is a G, but this identification is a practiced guess, not an obvious trait of the note itself. Absolute pitch is a completely different and rare way to perceive music.

In a way it is surprising that absolute pitch is rare. The hairlike cells of our inner ears are arranged so that each responds only to sound waves of a specific frequency, each cell connected to its own nerve fiber that carries this information to the auditory center of the brain. It seems like the brain should be able to keep track of these separate pieces of information, and with a little musical training the brain could be able to recall which specific auditory cells were activated.

When I ask Gary what it is like to hear with absolute pitch, he offers a comparison from everyday experience: "Identifying pitches with perfect pitch is similar to most people's ability to identify a color by seeing it." As soon as a child is told that the color of a red ball is red, then they don't need to think about it when they see something the same color; red is simply red, certain and unchanging. There are shades of musical pitch, however, just as stop-sign red is slightly different than Coca-Cola red; Gary tells me that he needs to fine tune his sense periodically, as it tends to go a slightly flat over time. Other musicians report that with age the calibration of their absolute pitch drifts downward, but most of us would not be able to tell the differences that they hear. We can only envy their ability to know.

It seems like all of that specific pitch information is wasted somewhere in the brain. It isn't that absolute pitch is a luxury, or that we couldn't use the information. Testing suggests that bats, dogs, and other mammals have absolute pitch. We know this because a dog or monkey can be trained to respond to a pitch of C, but not to D. They can tell the difference in a way that most of us cannot. In similar experiments, scientists can show that birds do not respond to the song of another bird if it is electronically altered to start on a slightly different note. To us the transposed version is indistinguishable from the original bird call, but to the bird they are not the same thing. Birds don't transpose their songs to different keys, unless it is used as a special effect.

There is reason to believe that our Neanderthal ancestors also possessed absolute pitch, which may be a normal part of being a pre-verbal species (based on findings in humans with under-developed language capabilities). Many autistic musical savants have delayed speech development, but nearly all are able to name any note they hear without comparing it to other tones.

Most scientists also agree that infant humans are born with absolute pitch, losing it as they get older and wiser. As with nearly every human trait, both genetics and experience have a role in preserving perfect pitch in those rare individuals that retain the ability into adulthood. Early music training does make perfect pitch more likely; apparently the brain notices that identifying specific notes might have some utility when learning a musical instrument.

It is also known that young children who grow up with Asian languages like Chinese or Vietnamese are more likely to retain absolute pitch. In these "tonal languages" the meaning of a word depends in part on its pitch; the word "fun" means rice in Chinese when spoken in one pitch but has an entirely different meaning when spoken in a higher tone.

Although early exposure to music or musical languages increases the chances of retaining absolute pitch, there is also a genetic element; people of Asian ancestry are more likely to have the ability, even when they have never heard Chinese or Vietnamese. This raises the ever-present nature/nurture, chicken-and-egg question: Since there is a genetic component, sharing the genes for absolute pitch with other Asians may have tilted the development of language to use more tonal information. Or, being exposed to tonal language during the "critical period" of language and music development from birth to 6 years might prompt the brain to pay more attention to fine pitch distinctions. Relatives of non-Asians with absolute pitch also have a higher incidence of perfect pitch, so there are a number of factors at work.

My friend Gary is of Chinese ancestry, and he heard Cantonese spoken by uncles in his house at an early age. He also took piano lessons at 4 years of age. We may not choose our genes or influences, but they become part of who we are.

If, as some suggest, we are born with absolute pitch, why do most of us lose it in early childhood? It seems like it might be a useful ability to have, even if we aren't destined for the musical stage. Steven Mithin, in his book "The Singing Neanderthals", points to the acquisition of language as the culprit. He compares these "pre-verbal" ancestors with modern pre-school children and non-verbal autistics and concludes that learning to speak is responsible for the loss of absolute pitch. Mithin uses this conclusion to argue that early hominids used music, not words, to communicate among themselves.

Others have blamed the loss of absolute pitch on the complexity of Western music, with it's chromaticism and shifting key centers (Bach's Well-Tempered Clavier takes his musical material through all 24 major and minor keys) or the adoption of the tempered scale (which alters the mathematical relationships between the scale notes). But whether modern music or language is responsible, only a favored few retain our ancestral power to discern pitches.

Perfect pitch is a mixed blessing for the musical; it certainly helps the improvising musician hear what their bandmates are playing in real time. And for all types of composers and songwriters the ability to simply pull out a sheet of manuscript paper and write down what they are imagining saves a lot of plinking at the piano. A composer should to be able to write down an entire score without playing it to hear how it sounds, but when I try it the music sounds nothing like I expected.

There are drawbacks to absolute pitch as well: Musicians who hear the notes as distinct entities struggle when they have to transpose to a different key. The folk singer who uses a capo on her guitar to change the key to suit her voice might feel conflicted when she plays a C chord, but hears an Eb chord when she puts her capo at the 3rd fret.

Even non-musicians report that absolute pitch can decrease their musical enjoyment, as the constant labelling of the notes can obscure the beauty and power of the music.

Absolute pitch is no measure of musical ability, but the advantages must outweigh the drawbacks for musicians. The list of famous artists with the ability is long and stellar: Old guys, like Mozart, Beethoven, Chopin, and Handel are presumed to have had it, based on what we know of them. Great singers with the gift include Ella Fitzgerald, Bing Crosby, Mariah Carey, and Michael Jackson. Jimi Hendrix had perfect pitch, which may have helped him learn to his unique left-handed style which put the guitar strings in re-

verse order.   Gary Burton, a prodigy who became the greatest jazz vibraphonist of his generation, had perfect pitch until he lost it after a prolonged open heart surgery; he could
still play, but he had to do without one of his musical tools.

Duke Ellington was one of many musicians with perfect pitch. While his band was on tour he would write music
while lounging in his hotel room bathtub, handing out the
horn parts out to his musicians so that they could play the
music for him while he relaxed. But Ellington had an even
stranger gift: Every note had its own color and texture, as
real to him as the frequency of the pitches. The note D, for
instance, he described as feeling like dark blue burlap.
Ellington wrote with his musicians in mind, and when alto
saxophonist Johnny Hodges played a G, to him it felt like
blue satin: Color, texture, and music combined.

The mixing of sensations is termed synesthesia, which
is described both as a gift and as a neurologic "condition".
Some synesthetes report a fusing of taste and touch, as when
the taste of lemon triggers a tactile sensation of spiky. Others
actually see letters in different colors, A as red, B as green.
The most common form of synesthesia is chromesthesia, the
fusing of color with musical notes, keys, or instruments.

For people with chromesthesia it isn't just an association through experience or similarity. The sensation is automatic, unconscious, and usually present since birth. And
every person has their own unique association. Singer/
songwriter Finneas sees the note G as golden orange, while
Beach Boy Brian Wilson feels it as black. Finneas sees the
note E as orange, but perceives the key of E minor as red.
Singer and musician Pharrell Williams sees a rainbow divid-

ed into seven colors, with the octave of all the notes as white, and he uses his uncommon ability when playing and producing music. "It is the only way that I can identify what something sounds like. I know when something is in key because it either matches or doesn't; it feels different and it doesn't feel right." Composer and pianist Franz Liszt, who like many synesthetes may not have understood that others did not experience music as he did, would ask musicians in his orchestra to "play that section more blue".

Billy Joel's synesthesia is even more complicated. Entire songs come to him in their own combinations of hues. Typically, ballads shimmer in blues and greens, while strident rock tunes are fiery reds and oranges. When a lyric line ends in a vowel, it pulls the music toward green or blue. Strong rhythmic patterns appear to him as red and gold. His synesthesia is present even when he is sleeping, and he reports that some of his famous hits came fully and colorfully formed from his dreams.

As with absolute pitch, there is no shortage of famous people who share this rare ability (which has been termed a "neurologic condition", hinting at stigma, while others might view it more as a superpower.) Synesthesia is more common in artistic people, but like absolute pitch it is difficult to know whether people with mixed sensory perception are more drawn to creative pursuits, or whether artistic types are simply more willing to admit to strange perceptions than their athletic classmates. (I try to imagine the basketball player who sees the game clock changing colors as the numerals count down—would you tell that to your teammates?)

Popular musical artists who admit to chromesthesia include Billy Joel, Pharrell Williams, Kanye West, Jimi Hendrix, Billie Eilish , John Mayer, Mary K Blige, jazz pianist Marian McPartland, classical violinist Itzhak Perlman, and composers Jean Sibelius and Franz Liszt. And each person with chromesthesia describes their experience differently.

From the many examples of famous musicians with synesthesia it might seem like every musician must see their music through colored glasses, but synesthesia is a rare trait, even among musicians. The usual estimate is that only one in ten thousand people experiences it, and it is more common in women than in men. But other experts suggest that 4% of normal people have some form of synesthesia, although many may not realize that others don't hear the world in color and they are reluctant to admit that their brains work differently.

It is hard to imagine how chromesthesia feels to the person experiencing it. Some report they see the colors projected as part of what they see in their field of vision. Others simply see in in their "mind's eye", abstracted from the scene that they observe. It may be distracting, but it doesn't obscure the image that the eyes record. Dev Hynes, of the band Blood Orange, sees colored streamers bouncing around his field of view, which he doesn't find helpful.

Unlike absolute pitch, chromesthesia isn't necessarily useful to the music listener or performer, although most consider the colors and textures to be natural and experiencing music without the hues would seem strange. Some musicians have embraced their extra ability, and used it as inspiration. Oliver Messiaen was one of the major composers of the 20th century whose works were inspired by his chromesthesia. He heard chords as combinations of the colors that he experienced and used these as source material for many of his compositions.

LJ Rich, a contemporary composer and technology journalist with perfect pitch and chromesthesia, takes it even farther; her synesthesia goes both ways, from music to visual colors and from visual images into music. To her, colors and images are not mere inspiration; instead, she can simply look at a color, an object, or a person and automatically turn them into corresponding melodies for her compositions.

The similarities between absolute pitch and color synesthesia suggest some shared neurologic foundation. Each is supposedly rare (1 in 10,000), but may be more common if we searched through human experience with an open mind. Both have genetic tendencies, and both may be normal in infants, fading during early childhood. Both are automatic and obvious, presenting without conscious effort. Brain imaging suggests hyperconnectivity as a feature of both. When babies are born, they produce an over-abundance of synaptic connections between brain cells, and the newly developed nervous system doesn't know what functions will be needed in this new life. This changes as life in the real world is experienced. At first, the sound of a mother's voice is mixed with the bright colors in the nursery, the smell of baby powder and wet diapers, and the feeling of a warm blanket. The most important stimulus gradually becomes the maternal voice, and the new brain separates that sound from the surrounding colors and smells by pruning away unneeded sensory connections (or by teaching other parts of the brain to inhibit the associations). With time the mother's voice becomes familiar and different features are extracted: pitch, inflection, and words start to emerge from the stream of baby talk and lullabies, and more separation occurs, more synapses are removed. Something is lost, but specificity is gained, preparing the brain to function efficiently in the world.

An alternate explanation is that the connections from early life are still present as we get older, but are suppressed by inhibitory neurons from other areas of the brain. Disinhibition allows these hidden connections to reach consciousness. (see chapter on acquired musical savants). For practical purposes the net effect is the same for both disinhibition and for hyperconnectivity.

Brain anatomists always ask: How are the brains of people with absolute pitch or chromesthesia different, and where does it happen? Functional brain scans show that both conditions show enhanced activation during music listening in an area called the Superior Temporal Gyrus, suggesting that this area provides connections between the senses. In absolute pitch, the enhanced activation occurs mainly on the left side of the brain, while music/color synesthesia shows a similar pattern on the right side.

These perceptions underline the truth that every person experiences the world in their own way.

In 1974, Thomas Nagel published in influential paper entitled "What it is like to be a bat". Nagel was a philosopher, not a naturalist, and he didn't really care about flying mammals, but he was interested in the subjective nature of experience. He argued that no conscious being can truly understand how another senses the world, just as we can not imagine how life would be experienced by a bat whose world is mapped in high-pitched echoes of its surroundings. Scottish poet John Donne wrote that "No man is an island unto himself"; true perhaps in the world of ethics and society, but when it comes to perception every man and woman really is an island. We all live in our own world, with only analogy and metaphor as bridges between us.

For ten years I had ignored my high-frequency hearing loss, until I relented and purchased hearing aids. Fifty years of working around barking dogs in my clinic and playing music occasionally dampened my hearing for high pitched sounds. I could hear most things normally (at least I thought so), but the upper frequencies which make speech intelligible were diminished. When I first got hearing aids I was told that things would sound different for a few weeks, but that my brain would then adjust and everything would sound normal. It didn't. I could understand speech a little better, but I discovered that there were a lot of sounds of which I had not been aware. Our aging SUV made an alarming repertoire of creaks, squeals, and rattles that I had never noticed before. My wife reassured me that it had always sounded that way and we did not need a new car.

Now music sounded different, and not in a good way. I found that Mozart's string quartets sounded tinny and sharp, rather than rich and vibrant. I even stopped playing two of my own guitars because they had upper overtones that made them too twangy, too shrill. I realized that those high frequency noises were part of the way that most people heard the music, but I found them unpleasant.

While I was learning to live with hearing aids, I also started to learn the violin (perhaps a bad choice for someone averse to high pitches). I could make my violin sound better (to me) by taking out my hearing aids, but worried that it would cause me to develop a screechy tone that others would find unpleasant.

Hearing aids changed my perception of music and forced me to discover that there was more to hear than I knew. How others around me sense the world remains an enigma. I still have no ability to imagine absolute pitch, and I keep my colors separate from my music. But that is just me.

10

GOOD TOGETHER

It seems like a simple question: Why do certain notes sound good together, and others not so much? I didn't expect to find God, Mathematics, and the Universe in the answer.

Looking for the solution to the mysteries of harmony leads directly back to Pythagoras, the fifth century BCE Greek polymath who is credited with being the Father of Harmony (as well as the Father of Philosophy, the Father of Mathematics, and the Father of Astronomy—all while leading a spiritual movement grounded in math and music).

Pythagoras was fascinated by how a vibrating string creates a musical sound, so he invented (or borrowed) a fretted one-stringed instrument called a monochord. He noticed that when the string was divided exactly in half it produced a note eight tones higher than the note produced by the full length of the string, and when both tones were sounded together a wondrous harmonic unity was created: The Octave.

Being the mathematician that he was (with his own self-titled theorem to prove it), he tried dividing the string in thirds, and then in quarters. The segments produced notes 12 and 16 tones above his octave, each combination creating a satisfying togetherness with the original string. This wonderful mathematical symmetry confirmed Pythagoras's belief that the universe was based on ideal numerical proportions, so he developed a system of musical tuning based on the numerology of these perfect intervals.

The eight-note interval between the whole string and half of its length is an octave, which our modern ears hear as essentially the same note, C to shining C, satisfying and solid. When the string is divided into thirds it produces a note four steps above the octave, G above the octave C, creating an interval of a "perfect fifth". The ratios of string length for C and G are 3:1, prompting Pythagoras' eureka moment: Pleasing intervals might be attractive because they express simple ratios of integers. When math is simple, all is right with the world.

With similar logic he established that the interval of a perfect fourth (C to F) demonstrated a ratio of 4:3. Thus the "perfect" octave, "perfect" fourth, and "perfect" fifth were the most consonant intervals. Searching for universal truths, Pythagoras determined that all scale intervals could be expressed as a ratio equal to a power of 2 divided by a power of 3, or vice versa. With that formula he could derive the degree of consonance of other intervals; a major 3rd (the warm sounding combination of C and E) had a ratio of $3^4/2^6$, whereas a diminished 2nd (C to Db) had a dissonant ratio of $2^{19}/3^{12}$. Our ears would quickly tell us that these two adjacent piano keys clash when played together, but we would miss the elegant math.

These were observations of a man who was a scientist of his time, and were based on segments of a vibrating string. He had no way of knowing that each note has a vibrational frequency ranging from 20 to 20,000 sound waves per second. As it turns out, the ratios of those frequencies agree remarkably well with the Greek master's observations.

Pythagoras felt he had discovered the secret to why pairs of notes sounded beautiful or ugly together, but there was a problem: The only musical instrument that could play multiple notes at the same time was the lyre, the small U-shaped harp made famous by the original lyre-hero, Orpheus. The lyre had only seven strings (reportedly tuned C, D, E, F#, G, A, and B), and lacked the eighth string needed to play the octave. Searching for perfect resonance, Pythagoras added an additional string to his lyre (and lowered the F# to F), creating the ability to play the octave C, as well as the perfect 4th and 5th. His addition was met with resistance from the Greek establishment, who considered the lyre to be sacred, as was the number seven (following after the seven planets in the heavens). The eighth string created a pleasing sound, but the number eight might displease the gods.

Fortunately, his people respected and admired Pythagoras, which allowed him to use his extra string and his mathematical formulae to create an entire system of modes (scales) to express both human emotions and the mysteries of the universe.

Pythagoras also claimed the power of different intervals and modes to heal disease and influence human behavior. In one case, a depressed young man was about to set fire to his ex-girlfriend's house as Pythagoras was passing by. Realizing that someone was playing a flute in the distance using an agitating mode, he asked the flute player to change his tune. The young man was cured of his anger, and he forgave his ex-girlfriend. Pythagoras used his system of consonant intervals for medical purposes, becoming the first music therapist.

The idea of consonant and dissonant intervals has been the foundation for all polyphonic music ever since, whether the intervals are heard in a handful of notes played on a guitar or piano, or in the combined voices of a choir or the strings of an orchestra. Although we have changed the fine details of our tuning system, the basics remain: The octave, fourth, and fifth are clearly strong and consonant, while the major and minor thirds (C to E, C to Eb) and minor and major 6ths (the inverse of the thirds, E to C, Eb to C) are considered "sweet" consonances, pleasing to the ear and filling the spaces between the perfect intervals to color their moods. The other intervals, minor and major 2nds and minor and major 7ths, are considered dissonant, grating to the ear unless used for effect or presented in a wider harmonic context. The interval that evenly divides the octave, the flatted 5th (or sharped 4th) is the notorious "tritone", considered so offensive to the ear that it was referred to as the "devil's interval" and banned from sacred music. But even the devil deserves his due, and all Western music uses the tritone to create harmonic interest.

In contemplating the role of dissonance, the usual explanation is that these uneasy combinations create tension, inviting a satisfying resolution; what is a story without a crisis leading to a happy ending? The most used tension/resolution device in Western music uses the dissonant tritone of F and B to create teeth-gnashing tension until the notes move a half step in opposite directions to the beautifully consonant E and C. Happily ever after. Not all stories are that simple, however.

Pythagoras and his math aside, scientists have wondered whether we are really hard-wired to like intervals that contain simple ratios, or whether we learn to prefer the sounds of constant intervals from the music that we hear around us.

In the best scientific tradition, researchers decided to get some kids and some monkeys to investigate. They measured how long infants looked at speakers playing different intervals to measure their likes, and indeed the babies obliged by staring longer at consonant sounds. What about other primates? Different species of apes and monkeys showed varying degrees of discrimination, but young chimpanzees and some other monkeys reacted in the same way as human infants.

If people and primates like to hear octaves, 4ths, 5ths, and other numerically proportionate musical combinations, why use dissonant intervals at all?

Twentieth century composers sometimes seem to use dissonance like stand-up comics use profanity—to add an edge to their art and prove that their creativity is wild and untamed, unconstrained by any sense of propriety. Just as we become desensitized to profanity that would have shocked earlier generations, modern ears have adjusted to the sound of diminished 2nds, flatted 5ths, and clusters of adjacent notes that sound like a raccoon walking across a piano. Listeners still hear the difference between consonance and dissonance, but they are more accepting of tones that don't play nice together.

When I took a second-year music theory class in college as the only non-music major in the class, I wanted to write something adventurous, hip and, well, dissonant for my final class project. The assignment was to write a four-part vocal composition using the rules that we had struggled all semester to learn. Rule One is that compositions should avoid parallel 4ths and 5ths in the lower voice, so I decided to break this rule by writing the lower two voices completely in perfect 4ths and 5ths that moved together. Buried in the lower parts, I hoped that it wouldn't be too obvious. The upper two voices were written with consonant intervals, but using an entirely different key a whole tone higher than the lower voices, which meant that two notes which were sharp in the upper part were natural in the lower voices. As intended, this created a sea of dissonant intervals as the music moved along. To offset the clashing notes I spent dozens of hours trying to make the movement of the notes so logical within their own parts that they would sound like they belonged, intending that the music would teach the ear of the listener to embrace the dissonances as the music progressed.

During the last week of the semester the entire class was asked to sight-sing each of the student compositions (a skill that had been taught in class, but I could never master). The class did a creditable job of singing through most of the other students' compositions, but they simply couldn't sing mine; they could follow the melody of each voice, but once combined, the dissonances disoriented them and they found it impossible to find the right notes. Finally, our professor, the chairman of the music department, simply played my music at the piano so that we could all hear what it sounded like, and he gave me an A- for the project. His only criticism of the composition was my ending: I had brought all of the dissonant voices together so that the final chord was a simple, perfectly consonant major chord. I thought that the surprise ending would be like the sun suddenly breaking through a heavy overcast, a little joke at the end, but the professor told me that after declaring independence from consonance through the whole piece, I shouldn't have given in at the end. He might have given me a good grade only because he knew that I was headed off to veterinary school and the music department wouldn't have to deal with me in the future.

I found my old composition recently, and honestly it wasn't very good, dissonant or not; it would have caused babies to turn away and cry and sent monkeys scurrying for the treetops. But dissonance can't be all bad, or only used for tension so that a final consonance sounds better by comparison. So, how it is used for the greater good?

Classical composers (whose main gig seems to be movie and TV background music) are adept at using just the right dose of dissonance for effect. Starship exploding, add a tritone and a cluster of adjacent notes. The composer's skill allows the dissonance to express the emotion of the action without drawing attention to itself.

Jazz players from the bebop tradition have a whole different harmonic system designed to make dissonance palatable, hip, even attractive. Dig this: Standard chords based on the usual scales include the consonant notes of the harmonic overtone series: Root, 3rd, and 5th. The seventh is dissonant, added for texture, but why stop there? If a chord can be built as a stack of 3rd intervals, why not keep going: The 9th, the 11th, the 13th? As the numbers go up, so does the dissonance, but the trick is that the 9th (D over a C chord) is dissonant when heard relative to the C, but since the C9 chord also includes E, G, and Bb, the D is also heard in relationship to the G (interval of a 5th) and the Bb (interval of a 3rd). When all of the chord notes are present the relationships create connections that reduce the dissonances to the role of spices in a complex recipe. Add one part dissonance, two parts consonance, and stir well.

Need more adventure? The most common harmonic resolution is the G7 chord (dominant, or V7 chord) to the C (the root, or tonic chord). The G7 is a tension chord, with a tritone (B and F) that wants to pull the harmony toward the consonant C chord. Jazz musicians notice that the same notes inverted, F and B, provide the tritone in a Db7 chord, which is about as out-of-place as you can get in the key of C. It is standard practice when playing bebop for musicians to substitute the Db7 chord in place of the G7 when heading for the tonic C chord, creating the delicious stew of clashing harmony that gives modern jazz its distinctive sound.

Blues and Rock use a more direct approach to dissonance. With roots in cultures that were not influenced by the mystical mathematician from Greece, different scales were developed by ear. The pentatonic scale, which divides the octave into five evenly spaced notes instead of seven, shows up in ethnic music from all corners of the globe. Even Stone Age bone flutes had only five holes. As one culture influenced another (African influences meeting European instruments in America), the scales had some differences to work out. The root, 4th, and 5th intervals were in rough agreement, but the 2nd and 3rd notes had to merge into a new note somewhere south of the European major 3rd. Similarly, the 6th and 7th notes of the major scale had to compromise to become the 5th note of the pentatonic scale). These in-between notes (which aren't found on the piano keyboard or the woodwinds' keys and buttons) create their own addictive form of dissonance: The "blue note".

The mixture of the major third and the flatted third together (as well as the major 7th combined with the flatted 7th) provide the signature dissonance of American music, from the blues and jazz to Gershwin's Rhapsody in Blue. Since well-tuned European instruments don't have these dissonant notes built in, guitar players bend their strings across the fingerboard, horn players relax their embouchure, and pianists play adjacent notes (Eb and E together) to find that American dissonance. And listeners like it.

Here is the paradox: When presented with consonant or dissonant music intervals, listeners, from monkeys and babies to symphony-goers, claim to prefer the note combinations that have simple numerical ratios. And yet it seems that music could not exist without the discord of intervals that our brains can't compute. Musicians seem to be more sensitive to dissonant harmonies, and listeners become more tolerant of non-rational intervals as musicians use them more freely. Perhaps the preference for consonance is like a wish that things were simple, even when we understand that they are not.

Musicologists and anthropologists have repeated their consonant/dissonance preference studies in cultures across the globe, confirming consonance bias. But maybe, they wondered, the preference is learned. The harmonies of Western music are so ubiquitous that even the rural villager in India or the Malaysian islander has heard music from Western traditions (sadly, more likely Justin Beber than JS Bach) that extend all the way back to ancient Greece. Nearly every human brain on earth has been exposed to the simplicity of octaves, 4ths, 5ths, and their related consonances. So shared preferences might be the result of the harmonic diaspora of Western music.

In 2014 a team travelled into the heart of the Amazon to find a tribe that had never experienced Western-influenced music. In the remote Bolivian jungle a tribe called the Tsimane have lived for centuries with scant contact with the outside world. Although the Tsimane have their own vocal and instrumental music (which does not include harmony), they have little or no exposure to Western music, either classical or popular. John McDermott, a neuroscientist from MIT, joined anthropologist Ricardo Gordoy on a journey deep into the jungle by boat to test the preferences of the Tsimane people. They also tested other rural Bolivians, urban residents of La Paz, and American musicians and non-musicians. They found that the Tsimane showed no preference for consonant intervals (C and G) over dissonant combinations (C and F#). It wasn't that they couldn't identify both types of intervals, but they simply didn't find one sound any more appealing than the other.

As expected, other rural Bolivians had a slight preference for consonance, the urban Bolivians a bit more. The Americans all had a marked preference for consonance, and the preference was strongest among musicians. The conclusion that the team reached is that, despite Pythagoras' claims of a mystical universal human preference for the simple intervals of his lyre, our liking for the sounds of the simple major chord are a cultural artifact, rather than a hardwired instinct.

Our musical brain must be a blank tablet, eager to imprint to the first sounds that our infant brains encounter. If we filled the nursery with the music of Stravinsky or Cecil Taylor, our children might grow in the direction of harmonic complexity, tolerance, and diversity. But the tired mom might still be wise to use a lullaby filled with consonance to lull her fussy baby to sleep.

11

UNCERTAIN TIMES

In most things, wobbling is an indicator of weakness and instability. When your car starts to shimmy at 35 miles an hour, it is begging for an alignment. When the airliner on which you are a passenger trembles, the flight attendant reports turbulence and asks you to fasten your seat belt. And when your right hand develops a spontaneous tremor, your doctor suggests that you might be developing Parkinson's Disease. The needle on a seismograph, the flickering of a light bulb, the trembling lower lip; regular oscillations are usually an unwanted sign of trouble.

But when I sit and listen with my eyes closed to cellist YoYo Ma's recording of Ol' Man River, I hear each tone fluctuating slightly above and below the melody note, six times a second, and I am filled with a peaceful acceptance of the beauty and uncertainty of human experience.

We take vibrato for granted when we hear an opera singer, a violin soloist, a heavy metal guitarist, or a jazz saxophonist, but when we pause to think about the effect, it raises several questions: Why would we find this effect attractive? How does a vocalist or instrumentalist manage to tame rapid muscle tremors to produce a listenable sound? And why was vibrato avoided in music before the 18th century, but has become standard in many musical genres over the past 200 years?

Sometimes other effects are referred to as vibrato, but a true vibrato is a rhythmic fluctuation of pitch around a fundamental frequency. Desirable limits on vibrato are its depth (a fluctuation up to a quarter of a musical tone each direction for a singer, an eighth of a tone for an instrumentalist) and its rate (5 to 8 Hertz, or cycles per second, is considered ideal, although rocker Freddie Mercury's vibrato clocked in 10Hz).

Vibrato is sometimes confused with tremolo, a rhythmic fluctuation of the note's volume. My first guitar amplifier had a switch for tremolo effect, which gave a wavy sound that was characteristic of "surf guitar", the acoustical playground of the Ventures and Dick Dale. Tremolo (along with reverb) was the only sound-altering effect that we had for electric guitar in those golden days before fuzz-tones, phase shifters, flangers, and vocorders, so it was overused and is now called for only when a guitarist wants to evoke those bygone days of driving the T-Bird down to the beach on a Saturday night. But tremolo isn't vibrato. There is a third type of vibrato-like effect, in which the timbre of a note pulses rhythmically, and although this effect doesn't have its own term it likely adds to the complex envelope of a true vibrato.

Vibrato doesn't happen easily. I took a year of voice lessons after I was leading a contemporary church choir and our priest requested that I should please not sing at all. While I was trying to improve my voice I was also searching for vibrato. I am told that when breathing properly and using the right throat muscles, the voice will develop vibrato on its own, but it never happened for me. The scientific literature on singing (yes, there really is such a thing) suggests that most of the vibrato effect comes from a rapid reflex arc between two opposing throat muscles, the cricothyroid and the thyroarytenoid. One side relaxes as the other side contracts in a tennis match of nerves with the fundamental frequency as the net. But a desirable vibrato consists of oscillations that are perfectly timed in sync with each other, and taking turns is never easy,

Instrumentalists of all types strive to imitate a vocal vibrato on their instruments, using a variety of tricks and techniques. Violins and cellos almost require vibrato from any competent player, but like the vocal version, it doesn't just come when called. The hand motion is simple enough: the finger of the left hand that depresses the string slides along the long axis of the fingerboard, producing alternating frequencies just above and below the fundamental pitch. But small rapid movements are not natural unless one is suffering from some form of nervous palsy. Only by spending hours moving the finger back and forth in small increments do the muscles develop the habit, and when the ability to produce vibrato arrives, it is often sudden and unannounced; one day the up-and-down motion produces only a sound like a colicky baby and the next day, when you aren't thinking about it, there it is—a note that sounds like a violin. Then it might take years to refine the rhythm so that it isn't too wide and slow (termed "wobble") or too shallow and fast (referred to as "bleat", and often triggered by nervousness on the part of the player). In my attempt to learn the violin, it took six months of silently rocking my finger up and down the violin strings while I watched TV before a hint of vibrato appeared.

In the modern orchestra, the norm is for the strings (and the oboe) to use vibrato all of the time, while the other woodwinds to use it when directed, the brass to use it only on special occasions, and the clarinets use it not at all.

Horn players have a variety of ways to imitate the human voice: Pulsing the breath, wobbling the fingers on the brass valves, or moving the jaw and lips against a reed can produce a reasonable vibrato with practice.

Guitarists, of course, have their own thing, and they don't want to be left out of all of the shaking and quivering of the other instruments. Accomplishing the effect is not simple, however, and anyone who simply strums chords while they sing probably doesn't care. Classical guitarists who hear the gorgeous tones of a cello suffer from vibrato envy, but moving the finger slightly up and down the string has limited effect on guitar, since the exact pitch is determined by the position of the fret, rather than the finger. If the frets are high enough, however, the string stretches slightly more when the finger is moved up close to the fret and a pleasant (but subtle) vibrato can be achieved with a violin-like finger movements.

Most electric guitar players aren't really looking for pleasant but subtle. Because metal strings change pitch easily when pushed sideways across the fret (rather than up and down the string), rock players can effect a wide vibrato by "bending" the string rhythmically. The exaggerated hand and wrist movements have the additional benefit of looking dramatic to listeners in the audience. This wrist vibrato takes skill and practice, so there is an attachment that allows even the novice 14-year-old to add an intense shake to his shredding; in the 1950's, Paul Bigsby invented a hand-operated lever incorporated into the bridge that the electric guitarist can operate with the heel of his right hand to tighten and loosen the entire set of strings, creating an intense vibrato.

The only instruments that can't create vibrato with the hands or lips are the keyboards; waggling the fingers on piano keys has no effect. However, eccentric pianist Glenn Gould, reclusive classical superstar of the 1950's, would often pause and vibrate his finger rhythmically over a note after he played it, and suggestible audience members swear that they could hear a distinct vibrato from the piano.

Organists have their own great trick, the Leslie Speaker: A wooden cabinet the size of a small square chest-of-drawers features a pair of horn-shaped speakers mounted on a rotating platform and driven by an electric motor. This gives the organ's output a pulsing "Doppler Effect". (In 1842 the Austrian physicist Christian Doppler noticed that when a train was approaching, its whistle frequency sounded higher than it did as the train passed and receded into the distance.) Using this principle, the rotating speaker horn of a Leslie creates a rise in pitch as it spins toward the listener and a drop in pitch as it passes and goes around for another rotation. It isn't exactly human-voice-authentic, but it gives the iconic Hammond B3 the soulful sound that carries the weight of the blues. Without the Leslie, the Mighty Hammond would just sound like another roller-rink organ, with notes but no soul.

Electronic keyboards include a vibrato setting, which isn't very convincing, at least if one prefers the complex organic fluctuation of pitch, volume, and timbre of a voice or violin. It turns out that it is really difficult to imitate the way that our brains and muscles interact to create a human sound, and electronics just don't capture the feeling. Partly this is due to the way that singers and instrumentalists often start a note with a "pure" tone and relax into vibrato as the note is held, an effect that is hard to imitate electronically.

It seems that adding a little bit of rhythmic modulation to a musical pitch is a lot of work. One is led to wonder why it is worth all that effort. In my search for why vibrato is so sought-after, I found a lot of different answers. Too many. The more answers there are to a question, the less likely it is that any of them are true. At the center of this mystery is the perplexing observation that vibrato has only been deemed desirable since the late 18th century. Before that a pure tone was preferred and musicians that used vibrato frequently were frowned upon. Leopold Mozart criticized violinists "who tremble consistently on every note as if they had the palsy". Purity was paramount.

If vibrato conveys a "human touch" to the music, why was it discouraged in early music but increasingly encouraged over the past two centuries? Is it simply subject to the whims of fashion, immune to logical justification? Or are there reasons rooted in psychology, technology, or humanity?

Increased perception of volume is often cited as an advantage to using vibrato, and there is a simple anatomic explanation for this. The inner ear is lined with nerve endings attached to tiny hairs of different lengths, organized from short fibers (stimulated by higher pitches) to longer (activated by lower tones). If we imagine one hair per frequency within the hearing limits of humans, from 26Hz to 10,000Hz, then a perfect A at 440 Hertz would fire only the one hair assigned to that frequency. If we introduce a narrow vibrato, then hairs with frequencies from 435 to 445Hz would respond, multiplying the number of nerve signals ten-fold. A wide vocal vibrato of 13Hz above and below the basic tone would trigger 26 individual hairs to send their signals to the auditory cortex, cranking up the volume significantly. In addition, 10% more airflow is used with a sung vibrato than with a pure tone, so a soprano's voice with vibrato can easily pack enough perceived volume to reach the back of an opera house.

Did a need for volume come with venue changes in the 18th century? Rooms for musical performance changed along with society; at one time music was mostly performed in parlors and royal drawing rooms, but as the middle classes were able to attend performances, concert halls increased in size and vibrato boosted the volume to help fill the larger spaces. As big orchestras gained popularity, solo violinists were encouraged to use vibrato to stand out over the large accompanying string section.

In the early years of music recording, it was claimed that vibrato offset "microphone fatigue", although I could not discern what that is. It seems that if volume was the reason for increased used of vibrato, then its use should have decreased as electronic amplification became the norm over the last seventy years.

Emotional expression is also offered as a reason for vibrato's popularity. Early music emphasized restraint and beauty over passion. Even the dance pieces of the European court composers were sedate, with gentlemen and gentlewomen moving gracefully to a waltz or minuet. But then came opera, and with the rise of its popularity emotion was turned loose with passionate storylines, elaborate staging, and over-the-top vocal virtuosity. Vibrato became valued as a way to enhance the drama. Instrumental music followed opera; orchestras grew in size, and composers infused their symphonies with more excitement, encouraging the strings to add more emotion to their playing.

Classical music is certainly not alone in wanting to increase emotional intensity: Nobody heaps on the vibrato like heavy metal guitarists; if wrist vibrato and the Bigsby "wang bar" don't provide enough drama, a rocker might have to smash his guitar and set it on fire.

Once vocalists felt free to express emotion (and formal vocal training provided better technique to bring it out), vibrato became a mark of human-ness and was appropriated by instrumentalists who wanted to develop their own distinctive "voice" with the use of vibrato. Adding this effect may have become the musical equivalent of the "I am not a robot" click box that appears on our computer screen when a website wants to confirm that a real person is responding. Doubtless the makers of electronic keyboards and amplifiers will continue to improve their algorithms to create a more realistic "I am not a synthesizer" illusion, unless musical fashion reverts to using more pure tone. But for my taste the most unpleasant technique used in modern pop music is the artificial pitch correction used in the studio, which instantly calculates the singer's intended pitch and corrects it to a pure synthesized tone: "I am not a human".

There are other more practical reasons for vibrato, however. Ricardo, my insightful and long-suffering violin teacher, told me that vibrato is useful when finding perfect intonation is difficult; if I play a note that isn't exactly in tune (which is all of my notes except the four open strings), then adding vibrato allows me to make my pitch adjustments less obvious as I move back and forth to find the true note. The same thing is true for singers, whose vocal cords have no convenient markers to calibrate how far they have to stretch to the next pitch.

These essays are about music and the brain, so it is time to consider that the answer to the question of why vibrato is attractive might lie deep within our brain.

Electrical oscillations ("brain waves") in the cerebral cortex occur at different frequencies. The first such waves, designated alpha waves, were discovered by Hans Berger, the inventor of the electroencephalograph (EEG). The alpha waves of synchronous nerve activity occur most noticeably during peaceful relaxation with the eyes closed, as in meditative states. The frequencies of these brain waves is 8 to 12Hz, roughly the same rate as the oscillations added by vibrato. Could it be that the regular pitch pulsations of vibrato resonate and accentuate the alpha waves of the brain? Beauty must have some neurologic correlate, after all.

Returning to the unanswered question of why vibrato was avoided prior to the late 18th century, I propose a theory, a metaphor perhaps. The essence of vibrato is uncertainty. The pure note A vibrates at 440 Hz, but vibrato suggests that it might be 427 Hz; or maybe 453. Or 427. Or 453. Ambiguity and complexity replace the certainty of a single unchanging standard pitch.

Before 1800, our understanding of the world was written in certainty. Kings and popes had unquestioned, God-given authority. Men did men's work, and women did everything else. Life forms were created as they are, unchanging. Humans were male or female, binary from birth. And continents did not go drifting across the surface of the globe.

Over the ensuing 200 years, we have gradually accepted that everything is variable and inexact. Even at the most basic level of reality things move back and forth, rather than settling in an exact, measurable position. Physicist Werner Heisenberg's Uncertainly Principle states that even an electron which appears to orbit around an atom's nucleus is only an approximation; its position and momentum cannot be simultaneously determined. The electron is there somewhere, but cloaked in uncertainty.

Uncertainty is a part of life and reality as we have come to understand it. Rhythmic pitch fluctuations in music may be beautiful because life itself is inexact. Even when we know where our center is, vibrato reminds us that being human means that we live with a certain degree of ambiguity. Embracing the uncertainty of life brings beauty and richness to our experience.

12

AS TIME GOES BY

Passing the doorway of The Black, a "head-shop" near my house in the hippie surfing village of Ocean Beach, I was stopped by a sound from the past: Cowbells, one high pitched and one low, marking time in a steady "tic, toc" for eight bars, followed by an electric guitar twanging a distinctive introduction, a mordant turn of f#, g, f# in a quick single-string figure. The rest of the band entered and several voices declaimed the disenchantment of the times in a chant, more prosody than melody: "Time Has Come Today...". I stopped on the sidewalk to listen.

After two and a half minutes the voices dropped out and the cowbell continued its persistent tic-toc, voices chanting "Time!" every eight beats as the tempo gradually slowed to a moribund crawl, eventually subdividing the beat with three echoes following each cowbell strike. Time was slowed, stretched, and subdivided, until the band came back for eight minutes of psychedelic meandering, eventually winding down to another slow-motion statement of "Time".

Upon hearing this song it was obvious why I had not heard the Chambers Brothers' 1968 hit, "Time Has Come Today", for 50 years. Although the tone of protest could easily have come from today, the music could only have been from the late 1960's; the impatient youth of today would never connect with eleven minutes of cowbell, chanting, and psychedelic guitars.

What I experienced was a magic moment of time-travel: from the first tic-toc, I was transported back to 1968, my freshman year of college; demonstrators had filled the streets, even in the normally quiet college town of Pullman, Washington. The civil rights movement combined with anti-war protests in a sense of youthful urgency, with soundtrack to match. The sound of "Time Has Come Today" could be heard across campus, from the Student Union Building to my dormitory, where the protest song leaked out from under the doors of student rooms accompanied by the smells of patchouli incense and pot.

The ability of music to create associations with past events ("They're playing our song!") is not new, but the ability of a simple cowbell tic-toc pattern to erase fifty years of intervening time caught me by surprise.

Time is a mystery without a satisfying explanation: It moves forward, never back, and although every person is aware of time passing, modern physics seems to say that time is an illusion. I once noticed graffiti on a restroom wall which claimed that "Time is just Nature's way of keeping everything from happening at once", which makes as much sense to me as anything.

Philosophers and psychologists attempt to explain our perception of time. Some claim that the brain has a sort of pacemaker which generates internal pulses to calibrate the duration of our experiences. Other theories suggest that the events experienced during a segment of time allow us to estimate how long it has been. Still others emphasize the limitations of short-term memory as the frame in which we perceive time. But in our everyday experience, music proves and defines the existence of time.

However we explain it, music exists only within the flow of time; melody lives because each note follows (and is separated by a time interval from) the next, creating a temporal relationship between the tones. Even if time is an illusion, we have no choice but to embrace the illusion.

One of the boldest experiments in music and the perception of time took place in Woodstock, New York. Although there may have been many warped perceptions of time at the festival on Yasgur's Farm in 1969, this experiment took place 15 years earlier in a tiny concert space on a dirt road near town. A small crowd came to hear acclaimed pianist David Tudor present a new piece of music. The pianist came out in tux and tails, seated himself at the shiny black grand piano, and placed six pages of music on the piano's music stand—blank pages.

He started a stopwatch on the bench next to him, closed the cover of the keyboard, and sat motionless for the next thirty seconds. The audience was mystified, and a few rose and walked out quietly. Tudor opened the cover of the keyboard, rearranged the blank pages on the stand, and closed the cover again. After 2 minutes and 23 seconds the sequence was repeated, and at the end of 4 minutes and 33 seconds he opened the keyboard cover, gathered the pages, bowed, and silently left the stage. This was not what the audience had expected, but they had witnessed the premier of composer John Cage's notorious 4 Minutes and 33 Seconds Of Silence, in 3 movements. There was no ovation or encore.

Intense and acrimonious criticism followed this new "composition"; was it a joke? An insult to composers and musicians? What was the point of music if it only consisted of silence? But the silence wasn't really silent. At the beginning of each movement the cover of the keyboard made a click as it was gently lowered over the keys. The piano made no sound, but the footsteps of audience members who left punctuated the silence. Someone in the back row could be heard clearing their throat, trying to be inconspicuous. By the middle of the second movement those who remained started to notice sounds that are normally imperceptible: the rustling of the breeze in the trees outside and the whisper of the heating system. By the third movement audience members noticed the sounds of their breathing and felt as if they heard their own hearts dividing the time with a steady pulse.

Even now the meaning of Cage's provocative piece is argued over. At first it seemed to be a protest against the lack of silence and the intrusive ubiquitousness of music in modern life, and against Muzak in particular. Our world was becoming more filled with constant sensory stimulation and people started to wonder what we were missing. In the early 1950s experimenters placed people in dark, soundproof tanks of lukewarm water to find out what complete sensory deprivation felt like. With no stimulation, the brain starts to generate its own sensations, even causing hallucinations within a short period of time. By the 1960s other means of generating hallucinations took the place of the sensory deprivation tanks, but the brain's biologic need for novelty was already evident. Cage's composition seemed to explore what happens when time is not filled with external stimulation. The more nuanced message is that we need to be more aware of, and thankful for, the rich orchestra of environmental sounds that surround us.

In studies of time perception, subjects typically underestimate periods of time that are "empty", with no memorable events, and estimate the duration as longer if more "events" fill the time. If this is true, one might suspect that the first 30 seconds of Tudor's performance would have seemed to pass quickly, while the third movement, filled with the awareness of shuffling, breathing, and heartbeats, would have seemed longer. Or maybe just the natural thought of "When will this thing ever end so that I can go home?" made it seem that way. I checked, and 4' 33" is available on both CD and on iTunes.

If events measure the perception of time, it suggests that time is the medium in which the perception of music is rooted as well. Only by holding the musical events in memory can they be placed into a framework of time. Composers (and skilled improvisors) can manipulate time by teasing our memory to achieve their desired effects.

Short-term memory (STM) in humans spans about eight seconds, what psychology pioneer William James called the "specious present". A musical phrase that fits within the extended present tense is easy to identify and remember. The limit of items that can be stored in STM is known to be 7, plus or minus 2, but if a sequence of notes (or numbers, or words) can be "chunked" into segments of up to 7 elements, each chunk becomes an element, expanding the number of items that can be held in STM to 7x7, or 49 items. Repetition of a motif or rhythm within a phrase serves to divide the stream of notes for easier processing, and if a musical phrase is simple enough that it doesn't need to be chunked it becomes even easier to hear and remember. In addition, melodic devices that "close" a phrase, such as a descent to a lower note, help by placing a phrase within the eight second present of STM. Repetition and harmonic or melodic stopping points aid in moving the contents of STM to long-term memory (LTM) for retention and development over longer periods of time. The clever composer will use these devices to his/her advantage if they want to build on a melodic idea.

But the limitations of STM can also be used for the opposite effect: Incidental "background" music in movies or television drama may need to provide mood and texture without distracting from the action by being memorable on its own. This can be accomplished by extending a musical phrase past the limits of STM and avoiding repetition or closure that might allow the listener's brain to chunk it into memorable pieces that have substance of their own. Memory can be evaded in this way, emphasizing the characteristics of the individual acoustic event without allowing the music to be remembered.

The limitations and characteristics of STM are inescapable; melody is trapped in time (or perhaps enhanced, as a painting may be more attractive if mounted within an ornate frame). Even individual musical tones live within a time frame that is dictated by the processing of our auditory cortex. If we tap our fingers on a tabletop at a constant rate of one tap per second, we hear a stream of discrete clicks. If we could tap faster, at 5 times a second, we start to have difficulty separating one tap from another, and if we increase the rate toward 16 per second a gritty buzz is perceived. At frequencies above 16 times a second, our brain performs a remarkable magic trick: The buzz of rapid tapping turns into a musical tone, the lowest C on a piano.

In his scholarly book, "Music and Memory: An Introduction", author and researcher Bob Snyder emphasizes this point: "It is important to note that, although the *only* thing that changes as we pass from below 16 cps (cycles per second) to above it is our own neural processing, the nature of our experience changes dramatically".

This fusion requires at least two similar acoustic events to create a tone. If both identical sounds are separated by a mere 2 msec, we can tell that they are separate events, although we can't tell which came first (the "threshold of simultaneity"). If they are from 3 to 25 msec apart we can tell which sound came first (the "threshold of order"). A chain of identical events will fuse into a single musical tone if they are separated by 50 msec. The acoustic events must be nearly identical, which accounts for the very slight delay when an instrument like a violin, guitar, or trumpet initiates a tone: it takes a brief moment for the vibrations produced to settle from non-identical noises into a series of identical events; the technical skill of the musician will minimize this brief moment of "attack" for each note before a pure tone is produced.

This view of time somehow creates a magical view of the universe in which we live. The cycles of planets and stars are measured in years and millennia, and if their motion produces individual bursts of energy at long regular intervals we are unable to perceive them with our senses. We can feel the ground vibrate under us during an earthquake when it shakes at one-second intervals, but we don't hear anything. But when identical vibrations reach 16 cps we hear music. Once vibrations reach 20,000 cps we stop hearing anything at all, (although many of our fellow creatures , like the bat, continue to hum along, even up to 200,000 cps). The vibrations of our world continue into the realm of physics, reaching 10^{14} vibrations per second at the atomic level. All this shaking going on, but music is trapped between 20 and 20,000 by the limitations of our brain's processing power. Perhaps there is still more music out there, beyond the borders of our senses—a universe of good vibes.

In my mind I play a thought experiment in which I attend the symphony to hear one of Beethoven's master works. Listening to the violins warm up, I try to hear the squeaky sound of the 3rd harmonic overtones of the high E string, 5274 times a second. Listening closely also I hear the double bass tuning its low E string at 41 Hz. The tympanist is testing his drums, percussive vibrations below my fusion threshold so that only a loud deep boom results.

The conductor raises his baton and the first four notes come forth: da-da-da-dum. This opening motif of Beethoven's Fifth, lasting 4 seconds, fits easily into my short-term memory; this phrase is followed by a repetition one note lower, ensuring that these two fragments are held in short-term memory long enough to be transferred to long-term memory, where they are held for reference during the remaining forty minutes of the symphony.

For two thirds of an hour the vibrations, tones, motifs, and movements extend across time, knitting the milliseconds and minutes into the story of a composer who lived 200 years ago. Time crosses two centuries to tell us how it felt to be Ludvig von Beethoven, and it stretches on into the future. The first movement of Beethoven's Fifth Symphony was recorded on a copper disc covered in gold and sent forth into space with the Voyager spacecraft in 1977. After passing by other planets, the craft was lost in space, carrying Beethoven's music as a message to other civilizations. Time will tell how far it goes and what other worlds would make of a series of vibrations in time.

13

THE PRICE YOU PAY

Our inner selves can seem as mysterious as the center of the earth. We can scarcely guess or understand where our passions and talents come from. It is as if we are the geologists of three hundred years ago, witnessing earthquakes and volcanoes but helpless to imagine how they came to be from deep in the earth. In previous centuries the movement of the earth's tectonic plates over rivers of liquid rock and a spinning core of molten iron would have seemed as fantastic as the gods hurling lightning bolts to bend humans to their will.

Anthony Cicoria is an orthopedic surgeon in a small town in upstate New York. During an outdoor family gathering in uncertain fall weather, Dr. Cicoria stepped into a nearby phone booth to call his mother. In an instant a bolt from the heavens struck the phone both, knocking Cicoria on his back, unconscious and barely alive. Fortunately, a woman who was waiting to use the phone was an ICU nurse, and her CPR brought him back from the edge of death. After he recovered his senses, Cicoria claimed that he felt OK and declined a trip to the hospital. His memory was a little shaky, but a follow-up MRI was normal and in a few weeks he resumed his work as a surgeon.

Three weeks after the event, Cicoria noticed a sudden change. He had previously been uninterested in music, but now became obsessed with classical piano. He ordered a stack of Chopin sheet music and started teaching himself to play. As he struggled to learn to read and play, however, he found new and different music, hearing melodies that had never been played before. He realized that the music was coming from within, original cascades of notes and melodies that were his own. Although he was not yet proficient at notating music, he labored to write what he was hearing into his own compositions.

Dr. Cicoria continued his profession as a surgeon, but music took over his life. He became proficient enough to play concerts of his beloved Chopin's music, as well as his own compositions. He felt that in many ways he was a new, different person since being lightening-struck.

Neurologist Oliver Sacks details Dr Cicoria's story in his book, "Musicophilia", along with other patients who developed strong affinities for music from "out of the blue". Dr Sacks searches for some neurologic explanation for his patients' sudden attraction for music. Although Cicoria's MRI images showed no organic damage, Dr. Sacks surmises that the wiring of some of his neurons may have been disrupted, and when the brain was "rewired", it formed more connections with parts of the brain involved with music. As a neurologist, Dr Sacks was familiar with similar "musicophilia" developing in patients with brain tumors or focal epilepsy in the right temporal lobes of the brain, as well as in fronto-temporal dementia, in which a diminution of language and abstraction in the left side of the brain 'uncovers' impulses and passions in the right brain, where most music lives.

What it felt like to Tony Cicoria was not a seizure or a brain dysfunction, but rather an "inspiration", a gift that came from something other, something outside himself, something spiritual. To continue the geologic metaphor, it was as if a bolt of lightening split his head, revealing powerful forces that normally lie hidden under the rocky crust of our everyday lives.

It is impossible to read Dr. Cicoria's story without wondering what passions and abilities lie hidden deep within each of us. But what if I suffered a blow to the head and woke to find that I was a fanatic about NASCAR racing or collecting Star Wars memorabilia? As boring as that seems to me now, perhaps there is some latent interest just waiting to be released. I just hope that it is something that I already like.

Although I have had an interest in music most of my life, I have never considered it a passion. Looking back, however, I see that there must have been some sort of fundamental attraction, at least to the instruments that produce musical sounds. The first time I bought anything with my own money I was six years old, visiting Anderson's Toyland in Denver with five dollars of saved allowance in my pocket. Anderson's would now be termed a superstore, two huge floors of everything that a kid might want to spend their allowance on. I ignored the toy trucks and Erector Sets and chose a set of rhythm instruments—wood blocks, maracas, a triangle, and a tambourine. I don't remember actually playing anything with my percussion collection, but I loved the idea that these pieces of wood and metal could produce music— even though I had no clear idea of what music actually was. I didn't try to learn an instrument until I took up the guitar in high school, and even then, I don't remember the sound of my first Gibson as much as I do the smell of the guitar's lacquer finish each time I opened the case.

It may be that musical abilities come with a price, and not just the thousands of hours of practice time needed to master an instrument. Perhaps something else needs to be missing to allow music to come forth.

At thirty-nine years of age, Derek Amato dove headfirst into the shallow end of a swimming pool at a party, his head smashing into the concrete bottom. For a moment he thought that he had died, but he managed to rise to the surface and a friend pulled him out of the pool. Gradually he recovered, but he refused to go to the hospital despite noticeable hearing loss and a severe headache. When his mother found about about the incident she took him to the hospital, where a CT scan revealed that he had suffered a severe concussion on his left side. Gradually he recovered (with the exception of frequent severe headaches), until a remarkable thing happened: Seeing an electronic keyboard at a friend's house, he was overcome with mental pictures of black and white squares moving across his field of view from left to right. Drawn to the keyboard, Derek started to translate the black and white squares into the black and white piano keys, producing complex classical piano music and astounding his friend. He stayed and played for six hours as the music poured forth, but he was unable to understand what was happening. The next day he dragged his mother to a piano store in an attempt to explain what he had experienced, and again he played spontaneous, virtuosic streams of music.

Amato had only casual experience with music in his past, playing a little drums and learning a couple of garage-band guitar chords. Nothing prepared him (or his friends) for this sudden ability to create and play complicated compositions out of thin air.

His ability persisted, and eventually he contacted Dr Darold Treffert, a neurologist who had consulted on the movie Rainman. After meeting Derek and taking a thorough history, a physical, and a few tests, Dr. Treffert concluded that Amato had Acquired Savant Syndrome.

Savants are noted for certain exceptional abilities, "islands of genius" out of proportion to the person's other functions. Some are mathematical prodigies, able to calculate large numbers in their heads or instantly name upon which day of the week any date in history fell. Others are gifted with artistic abilities, able to render uncanny drawings of a cathedral or an entire city after taking a single brief look. And some have musical abilities that seem to come from nowhere.

Savant Syndrome is usually associated with neurologic developmental problems, often some form of autism, and it is assumed that these children's brains develop in some unusual way to account for these abilities. In a small number of cases like Derek's the savant capabilities appear only after some damage to the brain. This might be due to "rewiring" as an area of damaged neurons releases a flood of neurotransmitters, connecting the brain cells in a more efficient manner. It may also be due to "disinhibition". Nerve cells don't just do things, firing off commands for action and cognition; 15% of the brain cells are inhibitory, firing to prevent other nerve cells from discharging. If (and that is a fascinating if) we are endowed with neurons that know how to calculate, draw, or play the piano, it could be that these functions already exist but are inhibited by other nerve cells. Once that control is gone, the uninhibited cells are freed to do what they want.

This is the part that haunts me: Are there musical functions hidden below the neurologic sediments of my mind that are teeming with melodies and music, just waiting to be freed? Do I have to stand in a phone booth during a thunderstorm to find out? And would the collateral damage of destroying those inhibitory neurons be a price I would be willing to pay? Anthony Cicoria

and Derek Amato insist that they would not give up their spontaneous talents, even if they could have avoided their brain in-
juries.

Not all sudden musical genius comes with a price. An Is-
raeli gentleman, known to medical literature as KA, had dabbled
at music, playing a little guitar and sounding out simple melodies
at the piano. At age 29, KA had an epiphany: While sitting at a
piano and plunking out a few simple notes, he suddenly "got it":
He understood the structure of music so deeply that harmoniza-
tion and the ability to recognize the intervals in a melody became
self-evident. In minutes he was able to play any song that he
knew and accompany it with the appropriate harmonies and
chords. After identifying the scales in all of the keys, he could
play any song in all of the different keys. When he turned to ref-
erences in music theory, he found that he already "knew" everything that the books contained.

Since KA had no developmental disorder and had experienced no trauma or infection, he apparently did not have a price
to pay for this musical expertise. He had a high IQ and worked
as an attorney, but soon was earning extra income playing music.
Some neurologists have termed this rare experience Sudden Savant Syndrome—others simply refer to "sudden genius".

Dr. Darold Treffert and others who have studied savants
suspect that some, most, or all of us have hidden abilities that
could be released. Studies using repeated Trans-cranial Magnetic
Stimulation (TMS) to suppress the left frontal cortex have had
mixed results. Using the ability to draw a figure from memory
(which is easier to evaluate than musical ability), 4 of 11 subjects
showed a major improvement in their artistic abilities after two
15 minute sessions of TMS a week apart. Not the dramatic re-

sults that had been hoped for, but a tantalizing hint that there is more hidden in our brain than we are able to access.

It begins to seem that people with extraordinary abilities and no impairment of other functions are the prodigies whose talents are so far beyond the usual that they are more akin to genius than mere talent. A team led by Mauro Pesenti and colleagues in Belgium and France used Positron Emission Tomography (PET scans) to compare brain activity in Rudiger Gann, a mathematical prodigy capable of astounding calculations, with other people of normal abilities. When doing routine calculations, Gann used the same areas of his brain (mostly in the left hemisphere) as the normal subjects. But when he was challenged with a problem so complex that it required his prodigious abilities, then his right medial frontal cortex took over, aided by a unique form of memory. Most of us store the steps involved in a problem in short-term memory while we work out the problem. In Gann, however, some of his long-term memory was recruited to provide almost unlimited capacity to hold information while the problem was solved.

Dr Treffert has studied savants for decades, and he notes that this use of an expanded, "unconscious memory" and right-hemisphere processing is reminiscent of the musical savants that he has studied. It would be interesting to compare the way that the brain of a musical prodigy functions with the mind of an acquired musical savant; Dr Treffert suspects that there may be a common mental pathway.

The stories of Dr. Cicoria, Mr. Amato, and other acquired musical savants have in common the sudden unquenchable ability to create original music, not just the ability to play impressively with minimal training. This seems puzzling: Is all of this music out there just waiting to be "discovered" by a receptive mind? Since music, despite its universality, is a cultural phenomenon, one has to think that all of the music that each of us is exposed to in our environment, from radio, television, or elevators, is somehow present in some part of our subconscious. The patterns and rules of music must be processed and stored as an underground source that can be released in a creative surge, whether we study for years to drill down and tap the source or it bubbles up, unbidden.

There is a story about JS Bach, when he was approached by an admirer who asked "How do you manage to think of all these new tunes?". Bach's reply was "My dear fellow, I have no need to think of them. I have the greatest difficulty not to step on them when I get out of bed in the morning and start moving around my room."

Prodigy or savant? Inspiration or genius? I like to think that somewhere deep below there is a hidden aquifer of music, deep as the earth, waiting to be tapped. Just knowing that the music is down there somewhere is enough to keep up the search.

14

ACROSS THE SPECTRUM

There was something different about the classical guitarist who walked out on the stage in the small junior college auditorium. I had never heard of Paul Galbraith, but my evening was free, and so was the concert. Without even a nod to the small but attentive audience (including, it appeared, every aspiring young classical guitarist in San Diego), he placed a wooden box on the floor in front of his chair, placed his instrument between his knees, resting it on the box, and started to play. The music was familiar, but Bach, Hayden, and Brahms had never sounded like this; full and rich, like a grand piano. And perfect. Not just perfect like a virtuoso who has spent his life honing each nuance of every note; this was perfect in a different way. The notes were crystal-clear; there was no audible sound of his fingernails as they plucked each string, no sliding as his left hand moved along the frets. The perfection was so complete that I was distracted by wondering how he accomplished it, but as the stream of notes flowed forth in smooth single lines with counterpoint and chords so transparent that each note had a life of its own, it was easy to get lost in the music. This was no ordinary guitarist, and no ordinary guitar.

Galbraith's guitar was a one-of-a-kind invention, with eight strings instead of the usual six. The extra string above and below the guitar's usual range made it sound more like a piano, or perhaps a harpsichord. Instead of holding the instrument across his left knee in the usual classical guitar posture, he held it upright between his knees, as cellists do. And like a cello, the instrument had an extendable end-pin that rested on the wooden box at his feet, which acted as a resonating chamber and projected the guitar's vibrations from below, as well as from the guitar's sound-hole. Glancing at the one-page program that a student handed me as I entered the auditorium, I saw that Galbraith had commissioned famed English luthier David Rubio to design an instrument to go beyond the limitations of the six-string guitar. They called it the Brahms Guitar for its ability to bring the classic composer's pieces to life.

With his guitar's unique history, I expected Mr. Galbraith to tell us a little about why and how he had come by his instrument, but after he had played for an hour without looking up he simply rose and walked off the stage. Despite the fact that he had not spoken or acknowledged the audience, nor showed any visible emotion during his performance, the concert was one of the most amazing musical experiences I have seen. As I left the auditorium, I knew what struck me as different: I had a distinct impression that the guitarist might have Asperger's Syndrome.

Too often speculating about the mental condition of someone who seems different is unfair. It shouldn't matter if an amazing performance, a scientific breakthrough, or a work of art comes from a person with Bipolar Disorder, Tourette's Syndrome, high-functioning Autism, or from a Neurotypical ("regular person"), but that doesn't stop people making judgements. Advocates for "neurodiversity" have insisted that the big tent of humanity has room for all, and we should avoid labelling people by how their brains work.

Child psychologist Leo Kanner coined the term Autism in 1943 for children who could not relate to others, were overly obsessed with items or activities, and avoided any change in their lives. He was focused on their intellectual disability and blamed their parents for being too detached and not providing needed affection. At the same time, Hans Asperger was seeing a similar syndrome in his young patients at the University of Vienna, but he was more focused on encouraging these children whose brains clearly worked differently to develop skills that fit with their abilities. Asperger didn't publish a description of his more broad-minded view until 40 years after Kanner, during which time the stigma of autism grew. During the 1980s and 1990s people began to realize that the label of autism applied to a very diverse range of people, from the non-verbal mentally disabled to the socially awkward but talented (a realization helped, no doubt, by the Age of the Nerds, when socially awkward but brilliant individuals like Bill Gates and Steve Jobs changed our world and made being weird acceptable, even admirable.)

Despite its unfortunate and awkward history, autism has taught us that everyone is different, even among those diagnosed with Kanner's and Asperger's conditions. The current term, Autism Spectrum Disorder (advocates would prefer to leave off the "disorder" part, stressing that many of these people are not disordered, just different), reflects the diversity of people who share some of the hallmarks of autism. In common use the high-functioning end of the autistic spectrum is given the gentler designation of Asperger's Syndrome, and those who identify themselves as "Aspies" have become less shy about owning their differences.

With only a brief observation of Paul Galbraith, it would be presumptuous to assume that he has a place "on the spectrum" just because he is an uncommunicative perfectionist, and it is irrelevant to the magnificence of his music. But he does have a connection to one of the most famous musicians who occupied the genius end the spectrum. Galbraith has headlined festivals and organized tributes to Glenn Gould, the most famous and eccentric classical pianist of the 20th century.

Gould was born in Canada and became a child prodigy to whom the mastery of the piano came easily. He had both absolute pitch and an ability to memorize any piece and play it by simply reading the score, no practicing required. He gravitated towards the music of Bach and Beethoven and criticized what he considered the excessive showmanship of Mozart, Chopin, and Rachmaninoff. Gould's recordings of JS Bach's Goldberg Variations are considered accomplishments that will never be equaled.

His list of eccentricities is legendary. Gould sat very low to the piano on a short wooden chair that his father built for him after a childhood injury. His unusual posture brought his face almost down the to keyboard level, causing him to reach up for the notes rather than dropping his fingers onto the keys. He had the unconscious habit of humming along while he played, a habit he shared with jazz pianists Erroll Garner and Keith Jarret, and which drove his audio engineers crazy.

Gould was obsessive about his recordings; even with the tape technology of the 1950s he would insist on splicing in a single note to replace one with which he was dissatisfied. And his search for exactly the right Steinway with the perfect touch and tone drove everyone crazy, from his piano technician (who was often called upon the adjust his piano in the middle of a performance) to the curators in the famed New York Steinway basement, where concert legends came to choose their instruments. Katie Hafner details Gould's piano odyssey in "A Romance on Three Legs: Glenn Gould's Obsessive Quest For The Perfect Piano", and the pianist's impossible standards and obsession with his Steinway CD 318 make it clear that Gould fit all the criteria for Asperger's Syndrome, although the term had not yet come into use when Gould died in 1982.

It is likely that Glenn Gould's singular genius would not have been possible if he had been "neurotypical". His demand for a perfect, delicate touch allowed each voice in Bach's contrapuntal compositions to be heard, a quality evident in Paul Galbraith's guitar playing as well. Gould also shared Galbraith's search for the perfect instrument; Galbraith invented a new version of his instrument and a novel playing position, just as Gould would not play without his perfect piano and his short wooden chair. Gould also invented his own instrument, the harpsipiano (a cross between the piano and the harpsichord) to find exact the sounds that he heard, just as Galbraith invented a cross between the guitar and the cello. Galbraith's lack of interaction with the audience echoed Gould's violent dislike of performing on stage. The pianist once remarked that the ideal performer-to-audience ratio would be 1:0. Gould eventually quit performing in public altogether, even though he was the most sought-after concert pianist in the world at the time. He preferred to record in an environment where he had complete control, no audience, and the ability to create perfect pieces of musical art. Glenn Gould's music and his eccentricities were part of who he was and what he brought to the world, and a label of Asperger's neither adds to nor detracts from his genius.

There is a much lesser-known neurologic diagnosis that is nearly the opposite of Asperger's Syndrome, and it brings with it an almost magical attachment to music. William's Syndrome is a rare genetic condition that includes developmental defects (including heart problems), learning disabilities, and low IQ. But William's individuals are strikingly sociable and highly verbal, never without conversation and always with a story to tell. And they love music. Their affinity for music makes music therapy helpful in teaching them useful real-world skills. Affinity doesn't equate to ability, and there are no Glenn Goulds or Paul Galbraiths among them, but they often feel music so strongly that they are overcome with emotion when they hear classical music or listen to a folk singer with a guitar. And many do play instruments (although they can rarely read music) and sing songs. People with William's Syndrome often claim that music is a central part of their being; one said that "Music is my favorite way of thinking."

Williams Syndrome often comes with a characteristic appearance, including slender, pointed facial features and large eyes. Some anthropologists have suggested that these loquacious, delicately featured, and verbally creative people may have given rise to ancient stories of strange elves and fairies, sprites that were filled with magic and song.

The fact that both ends of our human spectrum, the high-functioning but poorly social Asperger's and the intellectually disabled but highly communicative William's, must tell us something about the place of music in our lives. Perhaps it is a river that runs deeply through all of us, but it has been partly buried by civilization, by literacy, and by the huge effort that it seems to take to live with each other. Maybe there is a story that needs to be rediscovered; To me, this river is what the music of JS Bach sounds like.

15

THE MUSIC IS GONNA GET YOU

Be careful. The air is alive with vibrations that might take over your body and soul, turning you into a genius or a gangster.

Music. It has become impossible to avoid it in a world filled with incessant pop tunes, elevator music, Starbucks ambience, TV music, and that sound pounding out of the car idling next to you at the stoplight. Add to those the tunes on your car radio, the heart-pumping music in your spin class, and the soothing sounds that pair well with your evening glass of cabernet. In an environment filled with all sorts of music, should we worry about the effects of what we listen to, or hope that the music is making us calmer, smarter, and healthier?

The effects of music on our health and behavior have become a favorite subject for researchers, with thousands of studies published (mostly by that strange species, the experimental psychologists). Not knowing whether I should be alarmed or hopeful about the effect of music on my mental health, I combed through hundreds of pages of studies on music and brain waves, music and creativity, music and violent behavior, music and blood pressure, music and substance abuse, and more in a random walk through the literature. The results were, as they say, all over the place.

Different genres of music would be expected to show different effects, and music choices often reflect the stylistic prejudices of the brain scientists. If positive, uplifting results are predicted, researchers will probably be playing Baroque classical music to their subjects. If teenage misbehavior is under scrutiny, the study will probably include heavy metal or rap. Sometimes the results have gone contrary to expectations, and sometimes the predictions simply become self-fulfilling prophecies.

Country music doesn't often show up in psychology experiments, but one statistical survey generated controversy when it was shown that in metropolitan areas, the more hours that white males spent listening to country music, the more likely they were to commit suicide. In fact, binging on country songs was associated with over half of the excess suicides among the cowboy demographic in cities. This correlation held, even after the data was corrected for divorce, alcoholism, poverty, "southernness", and gun ownership. It was unclear whether the figures were corrected by eliminating songs with divorce, booze, and poverty, or by disqualifying listeners who were divorced, drunk, and poor. One wonders how they purged these factors, and what country music was left.

In an unrelated "field study" in a bar, it was noted that when the tempo of the country song on the jukebox decreased, the rate of drinking increased. So that explains the guy at the end of the bar making notes on a clipboard.

In contrast to the few behavioral music studies involving country music, there is a wealth of data on heavy metal music and adolescents. Any parent who listens to their teenager's music might have reason to be concerned, and the American Academy of Pediatrics put forth an official advisory that stated the obvious: "A teenager's preference for certain types of music could be correlated or associated with certain behaviors." These concerns, along with an I-told-you-so attitude among parents, has emphasized the link between music, sex, drugs, anger, and aggression. Enter the experimental psychologists.

Several studies have looked at the link between anger and listening to heavy metal music. The test subjects were mostly young men with attitudes, and one experiment involved playing metal music loudly before provoking emotional responses to see if the kids were any more angry in the post-listening condition. Sounds like a fun way to spend an afternoon.

While there was increased emotional arousal in the metal-heads, there was no increase in anger. The control group of non-metal fans, however, showed significant increases in anger after the listening experience. The conclusion was that the effects of heavy metal depend on the individual's music preferences.

In another survey, metal music fans showed no increase in anger, but rated higher than non-listeners in anxiety and depression. These subjects were not exposed to the music, just asked about what music they listened to and if they were anxious, depressed, or angry.

Many of the studies involve asking people about their moods and music, but there is a scientific principle that states "correlation is not causation". It should not be surprising that depressed and angry people are drawn to depressed and angry music, even if the music doesn't cause the misery. One published conclusion was that "music was not a causal factor in youth acting out." Music preference was an indicator of emotional vulnerability, not a reason for it.

Even in the mental health realm, music preference reveals the person's mood and stability, but doesn't seem to worsen it. In one inpatient psychiatric program, metal fans were actually less likely than their peers to suffer from mental health problems, and their moods improved after listening to their music (unlike mainstream rock fans, whose moods neither improved nor worsened after listening to rock music). Even physiologic measurements like heart rate and blood pressure did not increase during exposure to Iron Maiden and Black Sabbath, at least among those who preferred them in their playlists.

Reasons for suicide are more difficult to study than overall mood, as it is hard to ask "What were you thinking?" One survey suggested that liking metal music was associated with having fewer "reasons for living" in males and more "suicidal thoughts" in females, but many of the kids in this study were dealing with serious problems at home that were far more significant than what was coming through their earphones.

Studies of moody teens are complicated, and results depend on which demographic slice is examined. For example, heavy metal listening increased depression in girls (not in boys), but only if they had depressed friends. Girls who listened to metal as an "avoidance" technique were more depressed, but girls who listened to the same music in a "problem-oriented" mode became less depressed (although what problems can be solved by Led Zeppelin is an interesting question).

One unexpected benefit of heavy metal music may be increased familiarity with the Greek and Roman classics and mythology. The classic languages, larger-than-life heroes, and powerful gods show up as frequent themes in metal music; someday the only people educated in the ancient gods and myths will be anxious and depressed teens.

Often it seems that the only thing that self-reported mood and music studies reveal is what kind of music people like to hear. But perhaps there are clues to be found by measuring neurophysiologic responses, heart and brain.

Heart rate is the simplest cardiovascular measurement, and neither classical nor metal played at different volumes seemed to affect it. A more sophisticated measure, Heart Rate Variability (HRV), is used as a measure of stress; the rest-and-relax parasympathetic nervous system acts as a brake on the heart and creates a slightly more irregular beat, so the higher the HRV, the more mellow we should feel. No effect of music on HRV was evident, casting doubt on the self-reported calming effect of music.

Blood pressure also seems like a useful number to check while a string quartet is playing in the background. One study from Indonesia reported a blood pressure drop of 21 points in elderly patients with hypertension while listening to—you guessed it—Mozart. Other data showed that both classics and jazz decreased blood pressure (when combined with medication); encouraging, but you have to wonder about a placebo effect of either the music the meds.

There are tantalizing claims in a number of other physical realms: Music increases lipid metabolism and lactic acid burn after exercise and helps regulate gastrointestinal motility, especially in cancer patients. Surgery patients dosed with classical music have less measurable stress and pain, both before and after their procedure, than patients that receive midazolam (a valium-like drug—which also has the effect of making patients unable to remember what happened to them, which seems like it might be a plus after surgery). In rats, music increased dopamine synthesis (via a calcimodulin-dependent system, for those who want to know). Perhaps the dopamine increase accounts for the beneficial effect of music in dopamine-deficient conditions like Parkinson's.

All well and good, neurologists might point out, but all that the cardiovascular system has to do is get blood to the brain. What we care about is what the neurons are doing. We should check out the brain to see what is going on.

Brain waves come in a selection of different Hertz frequencies (cycles per second), each with its own implications. Delta waves at .5-4Hz means you fell asleep. Theta waves, at 4-8 Hz, mean you are deeply relaxed and inwardly focused; you might be meditating. If the frequency is 8-12 Hz, you are in an alpha state, relaxed and passively attentive. And in the beta state (12-35 Hz) you are dominant, anxious, active, and externally attentive. Given these choices I might choose theta rhythm if I really wanted to chill out, but alpha waves seem like a good place to spend time.

The same study that recorded the 21 point drop in blood pressure found that classical music increased the alpha waves of the brain. Alpha waves also increased when subjects listened to classical and carnatic music (Indian classical, particularly the nasyid sub-genre). Many of the studies of music and the brain come from India, which may mirror Indian meditation traditions. Alpha rhythms decreased, however, when rock was played. When the tempo of classical music slowed to 60-80 beats per minute, theta waves started to increase, creating a meditation-like calming effect.

Since it seems that some types of music do indeed have "charms to soothe the savage breast", it makes sense that it could also soothe the savage beast, and indeed one well-designed study found that when classical music was piped into the high-stress environment of an animal shelter, the level of distressed barking declined and the dogs spent more time sleeping. When the music switched to heavy metal, the animals spent more time trembling.

In my own veterinary clinic we had a radio in the dog and cat wards, with orders to play classical music quietly at all times for the recovering patients. Since many of our kennel attendants were high-school and college age, the channel was often changed and the volume pumped up, so we had to intervene occasionally for the good of the dogs and cats.

Anxiety disorders are very common in dogs and I often recommend that my clients leave classical music playing for their anxious pet when they leave the house. This backfired once when a client left the FM classical station playing for her noise-phobic Jack Russell Terrier to mask any street sounds that might panic the dog. On the third day the dog's owner called to say that the dog had freaked out, chewed up everything in the house, and scratched up the walls while she was gone. I checked with the radio station: Yes, they reported, they had played the entire 1812 Overture that afternoon, cannons and all. Even classical music can't be trusted.

The weight of psychological evidence hints that music, even the music that drives parents crazy, isn't a major cause of the mental or physical ills of modern life. and even the dogs and rats seem to like it. If positive effects can be demonstrated, it might qualify Spotify and iTunes as humanitarian organizations. The benefits claimed by music researchers include improved mood, thinking, creativity, sports performance, and even con-sumer spending (if that can be considered a benefit).

People who listen to music a lot generally report that it improves their mood and decreases their stress—but only when the tunes are self-selected. You can't cure teenage angst or redneck anger just by playing Mozart. One study of "healthy university students" gathered more detailed data. Students listened to one hour of classical music daily for 60 days. and after two months there was no decrease in anxiety or increased feelings of autonomy. They did report more well-being and increased feelings of environmental mastery, personal growth, life purpose, and self-acceptance. For an inexpensive therapeutic, that seems promising.

Other cognitive benefits of music have not been as impressive as advocates have hoped. The so-called "Mozart Effect" of playing classics to children to increase their mental development and IQ has been largely disproved. A heavy dose of Mozart can cause improved spatial-temporal reasoning for the following 10-15 minutes, but it won't make a genius of your eight-year-old.

Psychologists have invented dozens of cognitive tests, and who better to try them out on than people listening to music? Iranian students showed improved reading comprehension while listening to classical music, and both classical music and jazz improved concentration in young Indian women. In the US, popular music distracted students on reading tests, while classical showed no change. On other cognitive tests, performance was enhanced by Indian classical and Indojazz, with a tempo of 120 beats per minute improving performance more than 85 or 180 bpm. The link between music and smarts may be stronger when students are learning to play an instrument. Seventh and eighth grade students who were taught jazz improvisation showed an increase in cognitive flexibility (8th graders) and improved inhibitory control (7th graders). When the number of class music credits were compared to achievement, the musicians had a slight edge, but probably not enough to push trumpet lessons on your high school child who would rather be out playing soccer.

Creativity is the holy grail of the 21st century workspace and playspace. Just having the right answers is no longer enough; what is needed are the right questions and out-of-the-box perspectives. Music might offer a way to juice up the environment and enhance creativity, but that isn't what researchers have found. Using psychological tools to measure creativity some research showed benefits: "Happy" classical music increased creativity scores in one group, but impaired creativity in others. Music didn't interfere with the work of creative individuals as much as that of non-creative people, but creative types tended to listen to more music while they work. One interesting survey used music to induce various moods. The group that was stimulated to be elated and the group forced to be depressed scored higher in creativity, while the group with mood-neutral music showed no result. Best to avoid Musak while you are writing your next screenplay. The lack-luster effect of music on creativity is surprising. The presence of varied audio patterns seems like it should stir up novel thought patterns, and the forward momentum of rhythm should pull the train of thought up and over the terrain of creative output. Disappointingly, the effects appear to be pleasant but unremarkable.

Athletes, on the other hand, are eager to try anything that might give even a small competitive edge. If cranking up tracks by Gloria Estefan or the Crusaders keeps you coming back to your spinning class every week or improves your free-throw-shooting percentage, it seems like an easy choice. If we hope to go faster, higher, or stronger while listening, research suggests that we need to be realistic. Studies attempting to show improved performance have mostly disappointed, although some specific measurements could point to helpful effects. Lactic acid buildup (thought to influence fatigue) was 20% less in a group that exercised with music, and risk-taking (which can pay off in highly competitive sports) increased with motivational songs. In cycling or treadmill studies, physiologic parameters showed more efficiency when the tempo of the music matched the tempo of the activity, and increasing tempo led to a quickening of pace.

Every elite athlete has their own music regimen that they feel prepares them to excel, but objective measurements seldom bear this out. It has been suggested, however, that music has the effect of separating thought from feeling, allowing the athlete to focus on their effort and not on how bad it hurts. Even the routine exercise class could benefit from perceiving less pain with more gain.

There is one area where the influence of music has significant effects: It can make you buy things. Without a doubt the commercial power of music receives lots of attention, but much of it doesn't make it into the scientific literature; advertisers want to manipulate us, not educate us. But psychologists have some interesting observations. Country music influences brand choice, but its power relies on conditioned responses and associations; look for it in truck ads that attempt to tap into the memories (real or not) of ideal rural masculinity. Soundscapes are an important ingredient in successful restaurants, where classical, jazz, and pop music increase the amount that patrons spend, while easy listening music is harder to digest. In web advertisements, vocal music (using either the original lyrics or ones altered for the product) has more effect than instrumental music or no music at all. We can be sure that advertising consultants know more than they are sharing about how music manipulates our spending.

After wandering lost among the literature on music's effect on our health, education, and welfare, we are back where we started. I would like to believe in the power of music to change our lives, but belief is a poor guide to the truth. The conclusion gleaned from the best work of musical psychologists seems to be: If it feels good, do it.

16

FOUR SHORT SUBJECTS

Crazy, He Calls Me

One of the popular historical pastimes of the 21st century is to guess what psychiatric disorder various famous people in history suffered from. Joan of Arc? At the very least she had severe migraines, based on the drawings of her visions of the "City of God", which look remarkably like the fuzzy circular "scotomas" of migraine. Saint Paul? Temporal lobe epilepsy seems a likely diagnosis, based on that Road to Emmaus episode. Famous Russian novelists? Clinical depression seems to be the norm for those writers. Abraham Lincoln and Winston Churchill? Depression, with a silver lining: depressed individuals are often at their best when a huge crisis looms.

Musicians provide fertile subjects for these posthumous mental diagnoses. In many cases their abuse of hard drugs obscures any mental illnesses from which the musical artists suffered: Charlie Parker, Bill Evans, Keith Richards, and myriad others may have been "self-medicating". Thelonious Monk might have been autistic, with his bizarre twirling during the solos of other musicians and his non-existent social skills. Monk's unique compositions even share some of the characteristics of drawings by autistic savants; angular, logical, and seeming to emerge in a finished, complete form rather than being gradually developed. Classical composer Robert Schumann likely suffered from bipolar disorder and died in a mental institution. And then there is Beethoven. Music and mental illness have often danced with each other.

I am pondering these thoughts because I recently read Wynton Marsalis' book, "Higher Ground". In his descriptions of famous jazz musicians, he laments the fact that John Coltrane, revered as the postmodern god of the tenor saxophone, was a severe obsessive-compulsive. According to Marsalis this was a tragedy, as it drove away other musicians who tired of his long, intense solos, and it alienated all but the most dedicated jazz listeners.

Obsessive-Compulsive Disorder does offer an explanation for Coltrane's idiosyncrasies. One of the reasons that he is so revered is that his practice habits were legendary. As a young man, he could be heard playing his scales even as he walked down the stairs to breakfast. He had a noiseless saxophone that he would take on airplanes so that he could practice in the restroom (try that now!). Even his improvisations embodied his compulsion to express every melodic idea possible. When Miles Davis asked him why he soloed so long, Coltrane responded that "I still had something to say, and I didn't know how to stop." Miles growled in reply, "Just take the #@*# horn out of your mouth."

If we accept the notion that this titan of avant-garde jazz suffered from OCD, what does that mean to those of us who saw a spiritual aesthetic in his impossible dedication to practice and his endless melodies and "sheets of sound"? Many of those obsessive characteristics actually made him into the unique musician that he was, but labelling him with a psychiatric diagnosis somehow taints the legend. When listening to his later recordings, are we hearing a transcendent genius, or simply witnessing the final train-wreck of a mental disorder?

There are those who suggest that we should accept all forms of mental illness as simply "neural diversity", similar to the racial and cultural diversity that makes our society richer and more complex. If nothing else, this suggests that we should be more conservative about medicating away those behaviors that fall outside the norm. And yet when we know someone personally who has a mental illness the suffering seems to outweigh any beneficial side-effects that might come with it.

Listening to Coltrane's beautiful ballad, "After The Rain", you can almost hear the peace that comes when the noise of an unquiet mind comes to rest. That may be enough of an answer.

Don't Think Twice, It's Alright

Creativity is one of the great mysteries of the human mind. Is it truly making something from nothing, or is it a process of throwing every previous experience into a sort of cerebral blender and then taking the top off to see what new combination splatters out? Brain scientists love to peer into the brain while it is working for hints about what the neurons are doing, and functional MRI reveals what part of the brain is working during different tasks.

Dr Charles Limb is a hearing specialist, surgeon, and brain researcher at University of California, San Francisco who also happens to be a jazz alto saxophonist. Musical improvisation seems to be an ideal window into the creative process, so Dr Limb rigged up a keyboard that a jazz pianist could play while his head and torso rested in the circular tunnel of the fMRI machine.

While the musician is creating jazz improvisation, Dr Limb notes that activity in the lateral prefrontal cortex is suppressed, while another area in the medial prefrontal cortex is activated. The functions of these areas hints at the nature of creativity. The lateral prefrontal cortex handles editing and evaluating, and this part of the brain is apparently taken out of the game during the heat of improvisation.

These findings provide neurologic justification for a variety of creative exercises. In the influential book, Drawing on the Right Side of the Brain, artists are told to copy figures that have been turned upside down so that they are less recognizable and inaccessible to the analytical brain. Novice writers often use an exercise called "timed writing" in which the person is required to write rapidly and continuously without pausing to think (or even to lift pencil from paper), thus preventing the the brain's editing function from engaging. Only after the writing process has generated a lengthy torrent of words is the person allowed to go back and edit what he or she has written. The common theme is that creativity requires temporary suspension of the conscious thinking process.

I have struggled for years to become a competent jazz improviser, with only occasional success. When I have had an opportunity to talk to good jazz musicians, I always ask them "what do you think about while you are playing". Most musicians are at a loss to explain their own creative process, but in general they respond that they don't think, they just listen and play. Somehow, they must learn how to turn off their lateral prefrontal cortex and allow their musical creativity to flow without thinking about it. This leaves unanswered the question of how musicians learn not to think.

Doug Miller, one of the premier jazz bassists in Seattle, told me a story that sheds some light on this process. When he was younger, Doug made the obligatory journey to play in New York City, a rite of passage for most professional jazz musicians. At one club in the big city, tenor saxophone legend Sonny Rollins hosts a weekly jam session and Doug was recruited to join the rhythm section. Saxophonists line up around the block to sit in and show off their abilities to the master by improvising five or six choruses over the chord changes of some up-tempo jazz standard. With as many as twenty horn players waiting to be heard, a single tune like Oleo might go on for two or three hours, a case of what Doug called "rhythm section abuse". For the first fifteen minutes, the hard-working bass player concentrates on playing the right notes, outlining each chord clearly at a ridiculously fast tempo. Eventually fatigue sets in and the bassist starts to simplify, using repeated notes and open strings to make the playing easier. After another fifteen minutes of struggle, a transformation takes place: Doug reports that a zen-like state takes over, in which the bass player is too tired to think or concentrate. The music suddenly plays itself and great bass lines are created without conscious awareness. This state of non-thinking is the nirvana of creativity for which jazz musicians strive.

Learning how to turn off the brain's critic in the lateral prefrontal cortex may take years of struggle, so any shortcut in this process would be welcome. Too many jazz musicians in the past have abused chemical substances in an effort to stop thinking, but now meditation has replaced medication for the many contemporary improvisors who use ancient Zen techniques to calm the overactive "monkey mind" that obstructs the flow of creativity. Newer brain studies suggest the possibility of using biofeedback or trans-cranial electromagnetic devices to retrain the brain, but somehow that seems like cheating. Eventually, creative musicians just need to relax, keep playing, and stop thinking about it.

Late Bloomers

Have you ever heard one of those teenage classical violin prodigies who is playing with a major symphony orchestra while their classmates are still learning to drive? What about that floppy-haired high school saxophonist that can outplay professionals twice his age? Well, I hate them.

Setting aside the old question of talent versus practice time, it just seems unfair that there are musicians who can play with awesome technique and sincere feeling when they haven't experienced enough of life to deserve an artistic voice. Therefore, I was heartened to read an essay by Malcolm Gladwell in his book "What the Dog Saw". He argues that some artists achieve greatness early, while others are late bloomers, and he analyzes the difference between the two.

Gladwell cites the examples of the writer whose first successful novel was written after he was retirement age and the painter who rose from decades of youthful mediocrity to produce masterpieces once his hair had grayed. If nothing else, these examples offer hope to those of us who have long passed the stage where we could become prodigies.

Upon analysis, the artists who produced works of quality at an early age seem to find their direction from within. Rarely do they report that other artists inspired them or informed their work. While arduous practice honed their skills, the content of their art seemed to appear fully-formed. This is reminiscent of descriptions of autistic savants, those mentally challenged artists or mathematicians who simply "see" the object of their imagination and record the images or numbers as they see them. One autistic child of 10 could sketch a Gothic cathedral in beautiful detail from memory, but when the sketching was repeated 10 years later it was no better and no worse. His artistic ability was a gift, but it did not progress or grow.

"Late bloomers" take a different course, according to Gladwell's analysis. Usually, these artists' initial attempts are mediocre and offer little reason to continue their efforts. But continue they do, experimenting with different approaches and looking to their external environment for ideas. Their gifts include diligent research to find new relationships in their material, weaving ideas together in different ways until gradually their works became meaningful and mature. These late bloomers bring more of the real world into their work as they gradually develop their skills and find what works and what doesn't.

The idea that artistic ability could be gradually acquired and improved over a lifetime is encouraging. But as I thumb through my "Listener's Guide To Classical Music" looking for biographies of famous classical musicians who overcame average youthful abilities to achieve greatness, I find that nearly every famous composer had already made their mark by their early 20's. I considered the jazz greats and failed to discover any players who labored in obscurity before developing a distinctive instrumental voice in middle age. Bill Evans described himself as a mediocre player who had to gradually work out every aspect of his piano playing for years before he could bring it to his performances, but even he doesn't qualify as a "late bloomer"; one of his most played compositions, the beautiful waltz "Very Early", was written as an assignment for a college music class.

This is discouraging, but perhaps it only means that fame is reserved for those musicians who can turn their precocious abilities into a successful career. Perhaps the musical late bloomers are forced to gradually develop their musical abilities while they are working day jobs and raising their families, squeezing in a few hours to practice after the children are asleep and searching Craigslist to find jam sessions and casual community orchestras. And maybe after their children have grown and left for college, the late bloomers take what they have learned over the years and create great music from their decades of experience and interrupted study. We probably won't hear much about these musicians, but their voices will be heard.

Play It Again

Aesthetics are intriguing. Beauty may be in the eye and ear of the beholder, but it must have a basis, perhaps even a function, deep in the neurons of our central nervous system. Recently I ran across an interesting assertion: According to one source, "The optimal percentage for the perception of beauty by the human brain is 20% redundancy". Twenty percent. A sort of "Golden Mean" of aesthetic repetition. This implies that people are attracted to a thing that repeats itself frequently, but not to excess. Perhaps when my children imply that my conversations repeat themselves, what they really mean is that my verbal redundancy has reached an unaesthetic 40% level.

The beauty of moderate redundancy actually makes a lot of sense. People tend to say "I know what I like", but they really mean "I like what I know." Our brains seem to feel happiest when novel stimuli are balanced with the familiar. In the visual arts, repetition is a frequent theme: A row of white aspen trunks, a trio of babies in flowerpots, or multiple spots of scarlet in an abstract painting resonate with our visual cortex. The Redundancy Rule gives us a mathematical means to evaluate art; on your next visit to the Seattle Art Museum, you might nod knowingly to a nearby art patron and comment that "I like it, but with 10% more redundancy it could be a masterpiece".

Repetition is a vital part of music. A small group of notes played in sequence becomes a motif, and this motif can be varied and repeated to build a beautiful composition. The trick is to find just the right amount of repetition. When I listen to jazz musicians with varying levels of expertise, it is evident that novice players often "wander around", playing lots of different notes that are technically correct (according to the chords and scales of the tune), but not very appealing. A great player can say more by repeating and inverting a phrase of just a few notes than an inexperienced player can express with a constant stream of unrelated musical phrases. More redundancy may be the difference between the banal and the beautiful.

The general concept of incorporating just the right amount of musical repetition sounds like a good recipe for beautiful composition or great improvisation, but it raises a number of questions; At what level(s) does this redundancy take place? By my calculation, a tune in AABA format (typical of many jazz standards, which consist of an 8-bar melody, a repeat of that melody, a different 8-bar section, and then a repeat of the original 8 bars) would contain an overall redundancy of 50%, since half of the song consists of melody that has already been played. Too much? On a much finer level, individual notes might be repeated without being recognized as redundant. (An old bandstand joke: A listener asks "Do you know how to play Stardust?", to which the bandleader replies "No, but we can play Bye Bye Blackbird, and it has a lot of the same notes in it.")

If we were to strive for that ideal 20% redundancy, which musical elements are eligible for repetition? Rhythm is just as important as pitch, after all. If we use entirely different pitches, but play them in the exact same rhythm as the previous musical phrase, is that 50% redundancy or none at all?

Tone and timbre are also essential parts of music; if the trombone comes in and plays the exact same phrase that the guitarist just played, it that 100% redundant, or just (some might say) 100% unnecessary? And where does that leave us with Free Jazz? There is no reason why totally free improvisation can't utilize the perfect proportions of repetition and variety, but many jazz experimenters seem to avoid repeating themselves at all. Perhaps that is why even the best free jazz players are heard to remark that the music is more fun to play than to listen to.

I thought of closing this essay by simply repeating the first paragraph for an aesthetically redundant effect, but that would be more echo than encore. Sometimes enough is enough.

EPILOGUE:

Thank you for listening.

ABOUT THE AUTHOR:
Dr. Lee R. Harris graduated the Washington State University
College of Veterinary Medicine in 1974 and spent the next 45
years caring for dogs, cats, birds, and bunnies at his clinic near
Seattle. He is also an enthusiastic amateur musician, playing a
wide variety of instruments in jazz combos, R&B bands, church
choirs, and community orchestras. Dr. Harris has published three
previous books about animals and veterinary medicine, as well as
an article in the Washington Post. He currently resides in San
Diego, where he writes, plays music occasionally, builds instruments, and spends time with his family.

Acknowledgements:
I owe a debt to all of the people who have shared their music
with me. Music is made of relationships, note to note and person
to person. The friendship and forbearance of music teachers,
bandmates, and audiences have enriched my life and taught me
the many lessons that music has to offer.

Thanks to Peggy Sue Kittrick for making my manuscript look
like a book, and to Colton Abbey for making a cover.

Made in the USA
Monee, IL
23 September 2021